AQA Advanced Maths

Mathematical Studies

Level 3 CERTIFICATE

Stan Dolan
June Haighton

WORKBOOK

Powered by MyMaths.co.uk

OXFORD
UNIVERSITY PRESS

HOW TO USE THIS BOOK

This write-in Workbook can be used with or without *AQA Mathematical Studies Level 3 Certificate Student Book* to help with your studies. It fully covers Papers 1, 2A, 2B and 2C and is split into two parts.

Part A is made up of **short activities**:

- These are broken down into topics and can be completed as homework, revision or as in-class tasks set by your teacher.
- For some of the more challenging topics, advice is given in hint boxes in the activities, and more structure is provided in the first activity question than you would normally see in an exam. Use this information to help you.
- MyMaths links are provided at the end of each activity to allow you even more practice.
- Use the check boxes at the start of each chapter to log your progress.

Part B is made up of **two complete sets of practice papers**:

- These are set out as you will experience them in the real exams.

Short answers are given in the workbook for you to check your answers. Fully worked solutions and practice paper mark schemes are also provided online at www.oxfordsecondary.co.uk/aqams-answers.

OXFORD
UNIVERSITY PRESS

Great Clarendon Street, Oxford, OX2 6DP, United Kingdom

Oxford University Press is a department of the University of Oxford. It furthers the University's objective of excellence in research, scholarship, and education by publishing worldwide. Oxford is a registered trade mark of Oxford University Press in the UK and in certain other countries

British Library Cataloguing in Publication Data

Data available

978 0 19 841709 5

10

Other books in this series:
AQA Mathematical Studies Level 3 Certificate Student Book by Oxford University Press
ISBN 978-0-19-836593-8

Paper used in the production of this book is a natural, recyclable product made from wood grown in sustainable forests. The manufacturing process conforms to the environmental regulations of the country of origin.
Printed in Great Britain by Bell and Bain Ltd. Glasgow

Acknowledgements

The publishers would like to thank the following for permissions to use their photographs:

p26: Dmitry Kalinovsky/Shutterstock; **p72:** Timothy Large/Alamy Stock Photo; **p105:** Robert Kneschke/Shutterstock; **p116:** Paul Looyen/Shutterstock; **p139:** chartcameraman/Shutterstock.

Extracts from government publications and Office of National Statistics (ONS) are Crown © copyright, and are used under the terms of the Open Government Licence v 3.0

Table of student numbers at Oxford, December 2015, from www.ox.ac.uk, copyright © University of Oxford 2017, used by permission of University of Oxford Information Office.

Figures from 'Petrol Prices', *The Times*, 15 Oct 2016, copyright © The Times 2016, used by permission of News Syndication

Contents

NOTE: Fully worked solutions and practice paper mark schemes are provided online at
www.oxfordsecondary.co.uk/aqams-answers

Sampling methods and use of random numbers

1 Sunita is investigating trains that arrive in London between 7am and 9am.

   (a) Describe the population in this investigation.

> Describe all members of the group being considered.

_____

   (b) For her sample, Sunita decides to investigate trains that arrive at Euston and King's Cross.

      (i) What type of sampling method is this?

_____

      (ii) Give one advantage and one disadvantage of this sampling method.

_____

_____

2 There are 24 students in a class. The class tutor wants to use random numbers to select five students. Describe how he can use random numbers to do this.

> Remember to say what to do if there are repeats in the numbers.

_____

_____

_____

3 After opinion polls failed to predict the Conservative victory in the 2015 UK general election, the Sturgis Inquiry came to the conclusion that 'the primary cause of the polling miss in 2015 was *unrepresentative samples*.'

What is meant by a **representative** sample and why is it so important to use them?

_____

_____

_____

4 A football team's fan club has 1.5 million male members and 650 thousand female members. The club wants to send questionnaires to a representative sample of 200 members to ask for their views on a new website.

> The number of females in the sample should be proportional to the number in the fan club.

How many female members should they include in their sample?

_____

_____

_____

5 A sample is to be taken from a school's sixth form. The head teacher decides to choose a sample stratified by gender and year.

(a) Is this a suitable sampling method to use? Give reasons for your answer.

_____

_____

(b) The table gives the number of students in the sixth form. Calculate the number of students from each category that should be included in a stratified sample of 30 students.

	Number of male students	Number of female students
Year 12	127	110
Year 13	103	94

_____

_____

_____

6 In 2016 it was proposed that Sherwood Forest Hospitals NHS Trust with 4500 members of staff should merge with Nottingham University Hospitals NHS Trust with 14 500 members of staff. A survey drew 420 responses from the Sherwood Forest Hospitals staff and 4060 from the Nottingham University Hospitals staff. The results were combined in a report which stated that the survey fairly represented both sets of staff.

Does the data support this claim? You must show your working.

Check for proportionality by comparing fractions, decimals or percentages.

_____

_____

_____

7 The table shows the number of staff working at a sixth form college.

Teaching staff	Office staff	Maintenance staff	Managers
87	56	15	12

The head teacher wants to find out the opinions of the staff about catering facilities at the college. She chooses four people from each category to ask.

(a) Give two reasons why this is not a good sample of staff to take.

_____

_____

(b) Give a full description of a better sampling method the head teacher could use.

_____

_____

_____

8 A company wishes to test a sample of the light bulbs it makes.

  (a) Describe the population in this context.

  _____

  (b) The production manager suggests that they test every 10th light bulb from the production line.

    (i) Explain why this does not give a random sample.

    _____

    (ii) Describe how random numbers can be used to give a random sample.

    _____

    _____

    _____

9 (a) Describe the way in which quota sampling is similar to stratified sampling.

  _____

  _____

  _____

  (b) Describe the way in which quota sampling is different from stratified sampling.

  _____

  _____

  _____

10 **Pollsters get it wrong again**

Before the June 2016 referendum, most of the national polls predicted an easy win for 'Remain'. However, the final vote was 51.9% for 'Leave' and 48.1% for 'Remain'. In November 2016, most of the polls in the USA failed to predict that Donald Trump would be elected as the next president.

Polls usually survey a sample of people online or by phone. Give reasons why these methods may not give results that reflect the results from the voting population.

  _____

  _____

  _____

  _____

Activity Sampling methods and
use of random numbers

11 A housing association sends questionnaires out by email or post to all of its tenants.

The table gives the number of tenants in each gender and age group, and the number who return their questionnaires.

Age (years)	Men		Women	
	Number of questionnaires sent	Number of returned questionnaires	Number of questionnaires sent	Number of returned questionnaires
Under 35	220	45	316	54
35–64	609	146	876	173
65 +	558	175	597	154

(a) The housing association claims that the returns have given them a representative sample of views.

Do you agree? Include calculations to support your answer.

_____

_____

_____

(b) (i) Calculate the overall percentage response rate.

_____

(ii) Suggest two ways in which the response rate could be improved.

_____

_____

12 Ofcom (the Office of Communications) monitors customer satisfaction with mobile phone providers.

The table gives market shares for the top three mobile phone providers in the UK in June 2015.

	Market share	Number of customers interviewed by Ofcom
EE	32.9%	198
O2	20.9%	138
Vodafone	18.2%	99

Source: www.statistica.com

Ofcom Quality of Customer Service Report 2015

Between August and November 2015, Ofcom carried out 551 interviews with customers who had contacted their mobile phone providers during the previous three months.

The table gives the number of these interviews with customers of the top three providers.

Comment on these data.

_____

_____

_____

_____

_____

Types of data and numerical measures

Paper 1 or Paper 2 common activity

1   A football club lists the transfer fees it pays in one year.

£750k   £5.02m   £3.4m   £26.5m   £3.15m   £750k   £1.25m

> Make sure you know the meanings of these terms.

(a) What type of data is this? Tick all the boxes that apply.

☐ qualitative   ☐ quantitative   ☐ discrete   ☐ continuous   ☐ primary   ☐ secondary

(b) Complete the table.

mode	range	median	interquartile range	mean	standard deviation

> Use your calculator's statistical functions.

_____

(c) (i) Which average do you think is the best representative value? Explain your answer.

_____

_____

(ii) Why might the football club want to use a different average?

_____

(d) Which measure in the table do you think gives the best measure of spread? Explain your answer.

_____

_____

2   The table gives the times spent by two doctors with their patients.

Time (nearest minute)		4	5	6	7	8	9	10	11	12	13	14
Number of patients	Doctor Brown	3	4	8	10	11	13	13	9	8	1	0
	Doctor Green	5	0	3	12	10	9	16	8	9	6	2

Compare the data for the two doctors.

> Use an average **and** a measure of spread.

_____

_____

_____

_____

> Mention the doctors when comparing the measures you have found.

3 The government asks local authorities to provide data for the weight of household waste they recycle.

   (a) What type of data is collected by the government? Circle all the words that apply.

      discrete   primary   qualitative   continuous   secondary   quantitative

   (b) The table gives the average weight of waste per person collected in EU countries in a year.

Waste w (kg/person)	$200 < w \leq 300$	$300 < w \leq 400$	$400 < w \leq 500$	$500 < w \leq 600$	$600 < w \leq 700$	$700 < w \leq 800$
Number of EU countries	2	6	10	6	3	1

Source: http://ec.europa.eu

In the same year, the average weight of waste per person collected in the UK was 482 kilograms. A newspaper headline says:

> The average UK person creates more waste than other EU citizens

Use the given data to comment on the newspaper headline.

_____

_____

_____

_____

_____

_____

4 Tansy and Rahid carry out a survey to find out how many minutes students spent on their mobile phones during one day.

	Number of students	Mean time (minutes)
Tansy	9	48.3
Rahid	16	54.2

   (a) Use the information in the table to calculate, to one decimal place, the mean time when these results are combined.

_____

_____

_____

   (b) One of the students was absent when Tansy and Rahid carried out their survey. The student says he spent three hours on his mobile phone. Do you think this result should be included with the other results? Explain your answer.

_____

_____

_____

_____

Box and whisker plots and cumulative frequency graphs

1 The table gives the ages of 15 women who attend a ballroom dancing class.

Woman	Sally	Jen	Carol	Fran	Ellie	Kylie	Wai	Val
Age (years)	24	36	51	29	19	34	27	49

Woman	Amy	Lena	Meera	Tracey	Kate	Astrid	Beth
Age (years)	34	28	31	25	43	18	23

(a) The table below shows information about the men who attend the class.

	Lowest age	Lower quartile	Median	Upper quartile	Highest age
Men	20	23	27	37	56
Women					

Complete this table to show the information for women.

> To find quartiles, treat the values either side of the median as a separate data set.

_____

_____

(b) Draw box plots to represent the data for men and women.

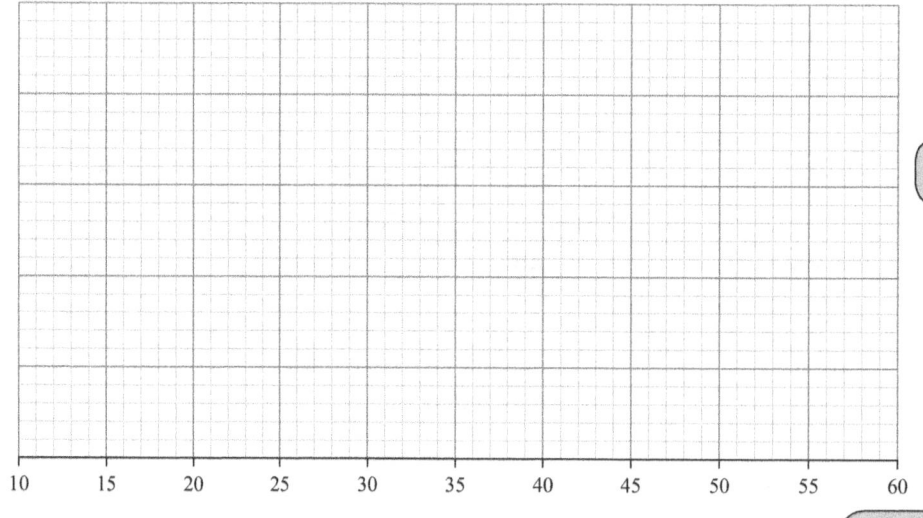

Age of men and women in ballroom dancing class (years)

> Remember to label clearly.

(c) Compare the ages of the men and women.

> Compare the medians and interquartile ranges. Remember to relate these to the real context.

_____

_____

_____

_____

_____

2 Lily and Simon carry out a traffic survey on a residential road that has a speed limit of 20 mph. They draw these diagrams to show their results.

Lily's diagram

Simon's diagram

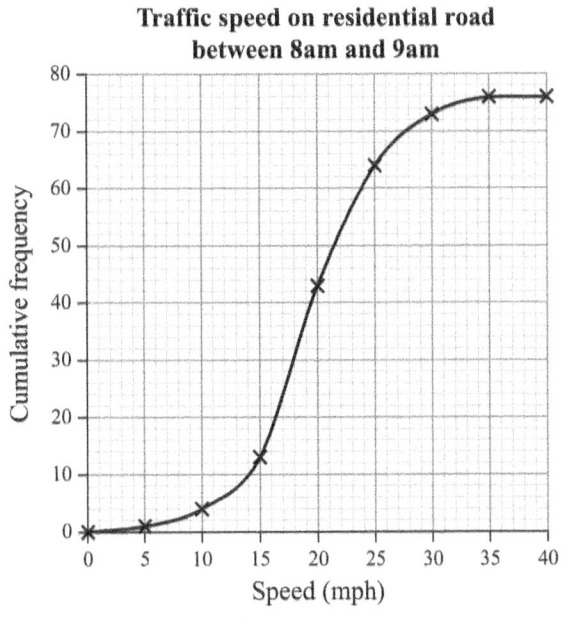

Traffic speed on residential road between 8am and 9am

Traffic speed on residential road between 5pm and 6pm

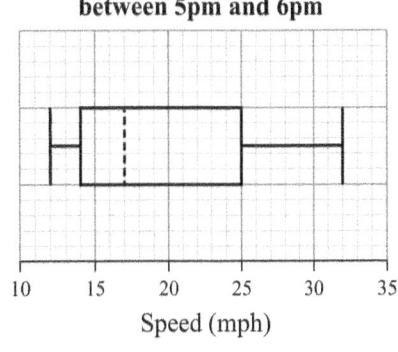

When n is larger than 20, find the position of the median and quartiles using $\dfrac{n}{2}, \dfrac{n}{4}$ and $\dfrac{3n}{4}$

(a) Use the diagrams to compare the speed of the traffic during these times.

_____

_____

_____

_____

_____

_____

Consider the information given on each diagram and how useful it may be.

(b) Comment on Lily's and Simon's choice of diagrams.

_____

_____

_____

_____

_____

_____

_____

3   The table shows the lengths of the discus throws made by women in the 2016 Olympics.
    The shortest discus throw was 43.70 metres and the longest was 69.21 metres.

Length, x metres	$40 < x \le 45$	$45 < x \le 50$	$50 < x \le 55$	$55 < x \le 60$	$60 < x \le 65$	$65 < x \le 70$
Number of throws	1	3	12	29	36	7

The lengths of javelin throws made by women in the 2016 Olympics are shown as a box plot.

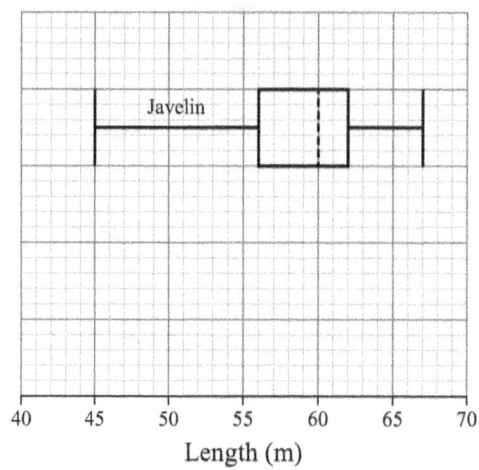

Length (m)

Compare the lengths of the discus and javelin throws. Use the grid below if you wish.

_____

_____

_____

_____

_____

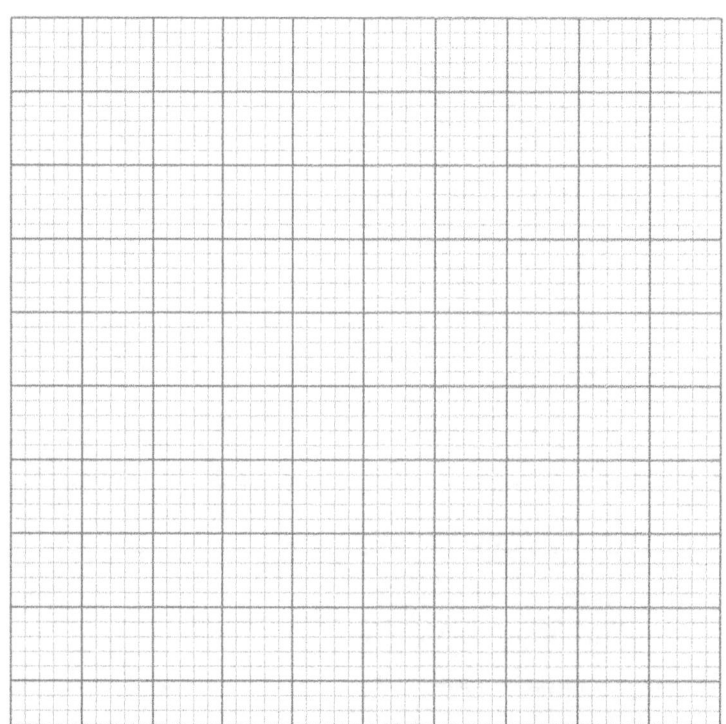

Remember to plot
cumulative frequency at the
end of each group.

Activity Box and whisker plots and
cumulative frequency graphs

4 The table shows the gross weekly earnings of the full-time employees of a chain of retail stores.

Gross weekly earnings, £x	Number of employees
$200 < x \le 300$	21
$300 < x \le 400$	74
$400 < x \le 450$	94
$450 < x \le 500$	75
$500 < x \le 550$	52
$550 < x \le 600$	32
$600 < x \le 700$	15
$700 < x \le 800$	11
$800 < x \le 1000$	5
$1000 < x \le 1200$	1

Compare the distribution of earnings in the retail chain with the results given below for all full-time employees in the UK.

Percentile	10th	25th	50th	75th	90th
Full-time earnings	£308.90	£389.20	£538.70	£762.40	£1057.70

Source: 2016 Annual Survey of Hours and Earnings (ASHE)—Office for National Statistics

Use the grid below if you wish.

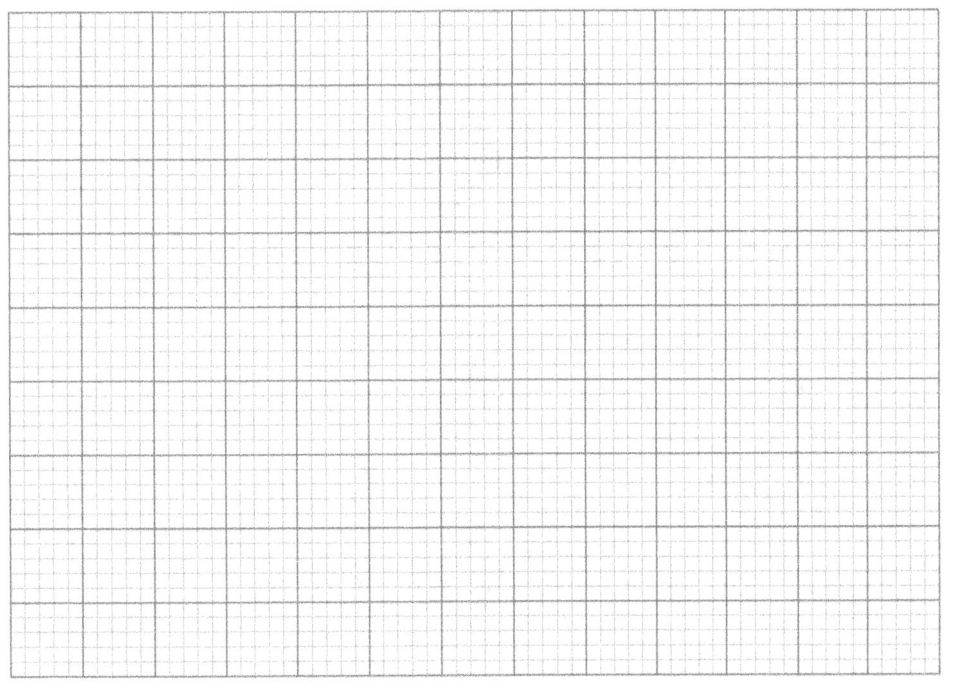

Histograms

1 Jack has started a histogram to show the age distribution of the population of Rutland.

Age (years)	Frequency	Lower boundary	Upper boundary	Class width	Frequency density
0–4	1766	0	5	5	1766 ÷ 5 = 353
5–17	5950				
18–54	16 322				
55–64	4907				
65–74	5013				
75–89	3600				
90+	488				

Source: www.ons.gov.uk (ukmye2015)

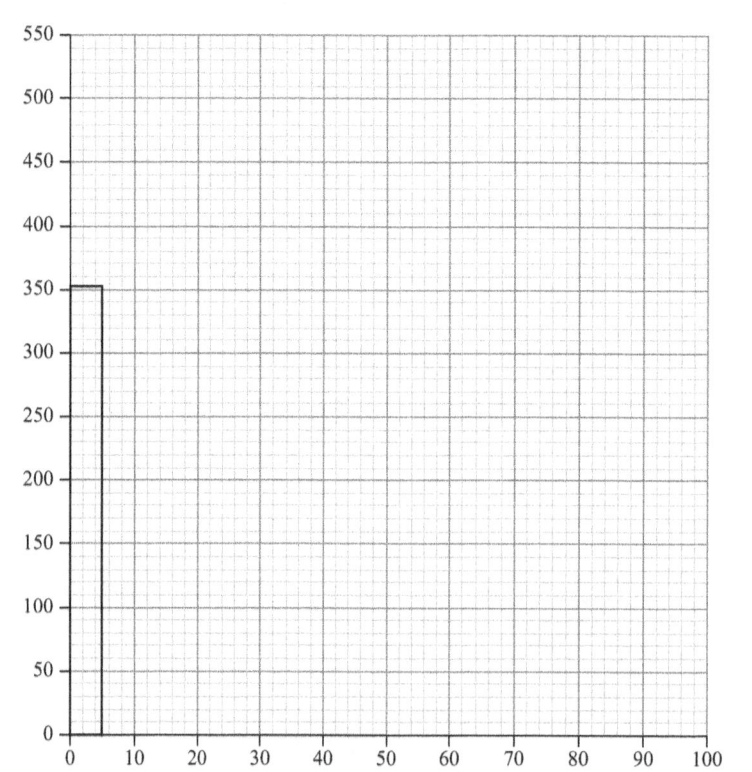

Frequency density is the number of people per year.

Take care with ages. The 0–4 group is a 5-year range.

Remember that area represents frequency.

(a) Complete Jack's table and histogram. State any assumptions Jack has made.

_____

(b) What does one small square on the histogram represent? _____

(c) Estimate:
  (i) the number of people who are aged under 20 _____

_____

  (ii) the percentage of the population who are aged 60 or over _____

_____

Paper 1 or Paper 2 common activity

2   The histogram shows the number of houses an online estate agent expects to sell in each price range
    next year. The estate agent expects that 70 houses will sell for less than £150 000.

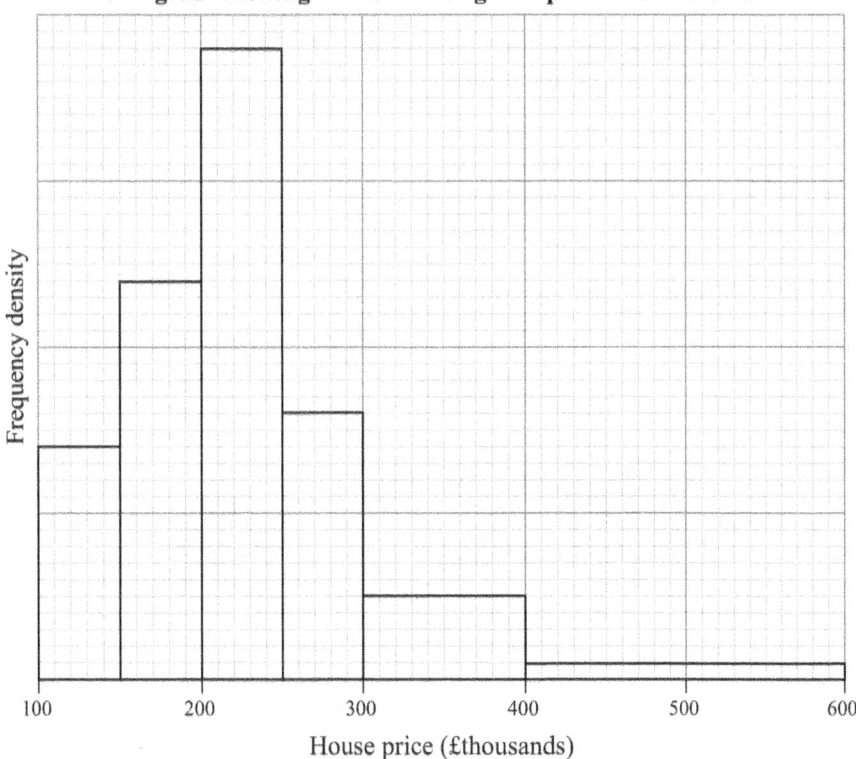

The table shows the fees the estate agent charges
for selling houses.

Work out how much the estate agent expects to earn
from his predicted sales.

House selling price	Fee
Less than £200k	£490
£200k – £$\frac{1}{2}$ million	£990
Over £$\frac{1}{2}$ million	£1490

Borrowing money

1 Karl borrows money to buy a new car at an APR of 20%. He has to pay back the loan in two equal repayments of £3600, the first after one year and the second at the end of two years. Find the amount of the loan.

> Use the APR formula.

_____

_____

_____

2 This form shows an application for a loan that has been partially completed.

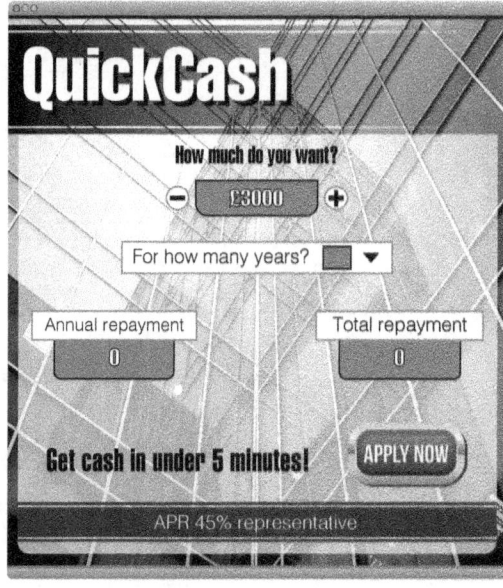

(a) What does the word 'representative' mean?

_____

_____

(b) If the borrower inputs '1' for the length of the loan, what would the annual repayment be – in other words, the single repayment after 1 year?

_____

_____

(c) Use the APR formula to complete the QuickCash form for a 3-year loan.

_____

_____

_____

3 The comparative costs of renting and buying depend upon where you live.

City	Monthly rent	Monthly mortgage
Cambridge	£1104	£1873
Newcastle	£591	£500

The cost of a 2-bedroom property

Source: Thisismoney.co.uk, 6 April 2016

(a) Suggest why a family in Cambridge might choose the more expensive option of buying.

_____

_____

_____

(b) Suggest why a family in Newcastle might choose the more expensive option of renting.

_____

_____

_____

4 Sheila pays a deposit of 25% for a £240 000 flat. The annual interest on her mortgage is 4% and she repays £1000 per month. This is a spreadsheet for her repayments.

Year	Initial amount	Interest	Repayments
2017	£180 000	£7200	£12 000
2018	£175 200		
2019			
2020			

(a) Complete the first three rows of the spreadsheet.

_____

_____

_____

(b) In which year will Sheila pay off the mortgage?

> You can use a spreadsheet to help with this calculation if you wish.

_____

_____

_____

Budgeting

1 Will and Kate are starting to save for a 10% deposit on a house. They are using a savings account at 1.5% AER. They aim to buy a £250 000 house in four years, when Kate has finished her degree. They use an online calculator.

(a) What do the initials AER stand for?

_____

(b) The monthly saving of £100 is not sufficient. What amount of monthly saving do Will and Kate need to make to reach their goal?

_____

_____

2 The account which is offering Will and Kate an AER of 1.5% also publishes a 'nominal interest rate' of 1.49%.

Show that this figure is correct and explain why the nominal interest rate is lower than the AER for the same account.

> Use the AER formula.

_____

_____

_____

_____

3 Steve deposits £2000 in a Best Saver account. It earns compound interest of 0.99% every 3 months.

(a) How much does Steve have in his account after 18 months?

_____

_____

(b) Find the nominal rate and the AER for this account.

_____

_____

_____

4 The Johnsons have a net income of £2000 per month. This is their typical monthly expenditure.

Housing/household	£440	Miscellaneous	£200
Transport	£280	Eating out	£160
Food	£240	Clothing	£120
Recreation	£240	Alcohol/tobacco	£40

(a) Without changing their expenditure, what percentage of their income could the Johnsons use to build up their savings?

_____

_____

_____

(b) How much will the Johnsons be able to save in their working lives? State any assumptions you have made and comment on the amount that they can save.

_____

_____

_____

_____

_____

_____

_____

_____

Taxation

See the Preliminary material on page 70 for a table of taxation rates.

Paper 1 or Paper 2 common activity

1   During the tax year 2016–2017, Donald was employed on a salary of £82 000.
    He had a personal tax allowance of £11 000.

    Split Donald's salary into the different bands.

    (a) Calculate the annual income tax he pays.

    _____

    _____

    _____

    _____

    (b) One of Donald's colleagues pays £1000 more than Donald in income tax. How much does she earn?

    _____

    _____

    _____

    _____

2   During the tax year 2016–2017, Ivana earned £920 per week.

    (a) Calculate the amount of national insurance (NI) she pays each week.

    Note that the NI bands are not the same as the income tax bands.

    _____

    _____

    _____

    _____

    (b) After a pay rise of 10%, find the percentage increase in Ivana's NI payments.

    _____

    _____

    _____

    _____

3   During the tax year 2016–2017, Sasha was employed on a salary of £27 600. She had a personal tax allowance of £11 000 and, each month, she paid £50 into a personal pension. Throughout, give your answers to the nearest penny.

(a) Calculate Sasha's monthly NI payments.

_____

_____

_____

(b) Calculate the monthly income tax that she pays.

_____

_____

_____

(c) Sasha has a large student loan and repays 9% of everything she earns over £21 000. Calculate her monthly repayments.

_____

_____

_____

(d) Copy and complete this payslip for Sasha.

_____

_____

_____

Employee No.	Employee	Date	National Insurance No.		
01234	Sasha	30/08/2016	AB123456C		
Payments	Units	Rate	Amount	Deductions	Amount
Salary	1	⬭	⬭	PAYE Tax	⬭
				PAYE NI	⬭
				Personal pension	50.00
				Student loan	⬭
				Total deductions	⬭
Tax period 5	Total gross pay ⬭			Totals year to date	
				Total gross pay TD	⬭
				Tax paid TD	⬭
				NI TD	⬭
				Pension TD	⬭
				Student loan TD	⬭
Tax code 1100L	Payment method: BACS			Net Pay	⬭

Student loans

Paper 1 or Paper 2
common activity

> Each year, 9% of everything you earn over £21 000 is repaid.
> 30 years after graduation, any remaining loan is wiped out.

'*There is a real risk it will very soon not be seen as financially worthwhile to go to university.*'

Anthony Seldon, *The Sunday Times*, 21 Aug 2016

'*The fear is misplaced. This is a "no win, no fee" education. Only those who earn a lot after graduating or leaving university will repay a lot.*'

Martin Lewis, *Student Loan Myth Busting*, Sept 2016

1 Beverley has just retired and has the typical annual income for pensioners of £15 300. Never having gone to university, she now has the time and interest to study for an English Literature degree. Give her advice on whether or not she should take out a student loan.

_____

_____

_____

_____

> The interest rate on a student loan depends upon your income. For incomes up to £21 000, the interest rate is simply the RPI and so the amount of the loan just keeps pace with inflation. For higher incomes there is a sliding scale, rising to RPI + 3% for incomes of £41 000 and over.

2 (a) Explain the statement '*and so the amount of the loan just keeps pace with inflation*'.

_____

_____

_____

_____

(b) What is the interest rate for someone with an income of £36 000 if the RPI is 1.6%?

_____

_____

_____

_____

3 At the start of a year, Clare has a student loan of £44 000. During the year she has an income of £33 000 and the RPI is 1.6%.

(a) How much does she repay that year?

_____

_____

_____

_____

(b) Find the amount of interest added to her loan that year.

> Use the information given in the box before Question **2** and Clare's salary to find the interest rate.

_____

_____

_____

_____

(c) Assume that her repayments will increase by 2% per year. What is the total amount of the loan that Clare will repay?

> You can use a spreadsheet to help with this calculation if you wish.

_____

_____

_____

_____

4 Comment briefly on your answer to Question **3** in terms of the two opening statements about student loans.

_____

_____

_____

_____

_____

_____

_____

Percentage change

Paper 1 or Paper 2
common activity

1 Amil buys football match scarves for £3 each and sells them outside the stadium for £P.

After a game, he reduces the price, £P, by 25% and still makes 50% profit on the cost of each reduced-price scarf.

(a) Show that the reduced price is £4.50 for one scarf.

_____

_____

(b) Explain why $0.75P = 4.50$

> The multiplying factor method is the best way to solve most problems about percentage change.

_____

_____

(c) What is the selling price, £P, of each scarf?

_____

_____

2 Amil buys souvenir badges for £2.25 each and sells them for £C. After a game, he reduces the price, £C, by 10% and still makes 20% profit.

Find the selling price, £C.

> Always break unstructured questions into easy parts.

_____

_____

_____

_____

3 The Wheelers sold their house for 25% more than the £152 000 that they paid for it some years ago. This selling price was 5% less than their asking price.

Find the asking price.

_____

_____

_____

_____

4 A group of workers had a wage rise of 5% in March and a further wage rise of 5% in September.
   Their new annual salary was £24 255.

   What was the initial annual salary?

   _____

   _____

   _____

   _____

5 The exchange rate of E euros to the pound increased by 5%. It then fell by 20% to 1.05 euros.

   Find the original rate of E euros.

   _____

   _____

   _____

   _____

6 The price of a litre of petrol fell by 5%. It then increased by 22% to 115.9p.

   Find the original price.

   _____

   _____

   _____

   _____

7 The cost of an item includes an import duty of 6%. VAT at 20% of this cost also has to be paid and the
   total charge is then £139.92

   Find the cost of the item excluding import duty and VAT.

   _____

   _____

   _____

   _____

   _____

Modelling and estimation

1   Why is stock control an important aspect of many businesses?

_____

_____

_____

2   The diagram is a model for the stock of an item held by a company. Sales repeatedly reduce the level of
stock to a minimum amount S and then a delivery increases the level of stock to a maximum amount $S + D$.

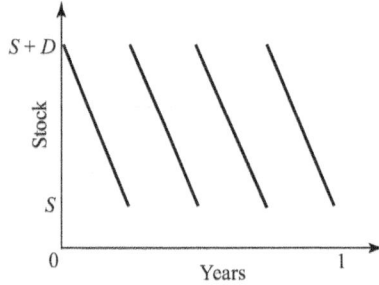

(a)   According to this model, what are the annual sales?

_____

_____

(b)   What simplifying assumption has been made about the sales?

_____

_____

(c)   What is the importance of the 'buffer' stock, S?

_____

_____

3 The annual cost of the stock can be modelled in terms of three costs:

- the cost, £A of buying each item
- the administrative and handling costs associated with each delivery, £B per delivery
- the warehousing cost, £C of keeping an item in stock for a year.

List some of the factors involved in warehousing costs.

_____

_____

_____

_____

4 A model for the total annual cost of the stock is:

$$£4DA + 4B + \left(S + \frac{D}{2} \right) C$$

Explain each of the terms in this model.

(a) £4DA

_____

_____

(b) £4B

_____

_____

(c) £$\left(S + \dfrac{D}{2} \right) C$

_____

_____

5 The model in Question **4** is applied to an item stocked by a large garage.

Annual sales of 1000 are expected. Roughly one week's supply, of 20 items, is kept as buffer stock.

The buying costs, delivery costs and warehousing costs are £100, £50 and £5, respectively.

Calculate the total annual cost of the stock.

_____

_____

_____

_____

6 (a) Complete this list of the factors which will affect the amount of royalties an author will earn on a textbook for a new 1-year course.

> Think of as many factors as possible. You can always ignore or simplify some of the factors as your model develops.

- Let the lifetime of the course (the number of years before it is replaced) be l years.

- Let each textbook last t years.

_____

_____

_____

_____

_____

_____

_____

(b) Construct a mathematical model for the total amount, £A of royalties.

> For difficult problems, construct the model in stages. For example, first obtain a formula for the amount the author receives for each book that is sold.

_____

_____

_____

_____

_____

_____

(c) Critically analyse the model in your answer to part **(b)**.

> For example, think of a complicating factor that has not been considered in your model.

_____

_____

_____

_____

_____

7 How many steps would it take to make a circuit of the Earth?

(a) State any assumptions you need to make.

_____

_____

_____

_____

(b) Make your estimate, showing all your calculations.

_____

_____

_____

_____

_____

8 How many small plastic toy building bricks are needed to make a full-size house? State any assumptions you have made.

_____

_____

_____

_____

_____

_____

_____

Critical analysis

1

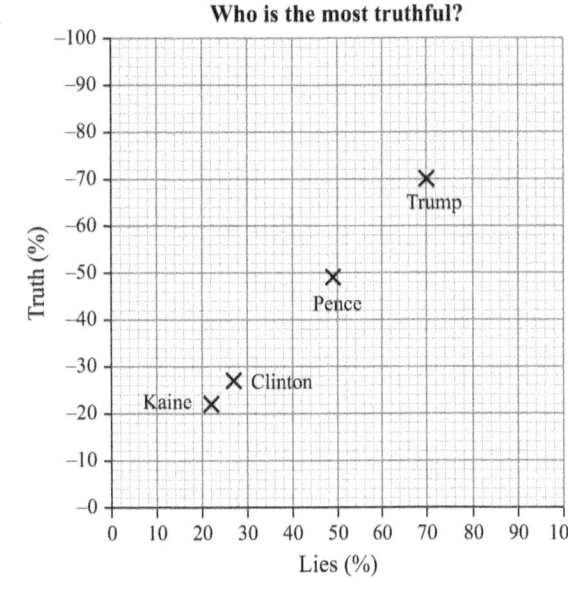

Who is the most truthful?

Source: politifact.com

(a) Critically analyse this diagram as a way of presenting the data about the statements of the American presidential nominees.

_____

_____

_____

_____

_____

(b) What does your answer to part **(a)** indicate about the website *Politifact*?

> Always read attributions carefully!

_____

(c) A friend says '*70 – 49 = 31 and so Trump lied 31 more times than Clinton*'. Criticise and correct this statement.

_____

_____

_____

_____

_____

2 In 1990, a trial published in *The New England Journal of Medicine* claimed to show that including oat bran in one's diet did not significantly lower cholesterol levels. There were 20 participants in the trial, many of whom were already interested in diets.

Comment on this trial and its findings.

_____

_____

_____

_____

_____

_____

3 In 1984, a study in *The Journal of the American Medical Association* found that low levels of alcohol intake by non-smoking pregnant women did not significantly affect the birth weight of their babies.

> Think about how you might obtain a representative sample of this population.

Why would a present-day study of this be problematical?

_____

_____

_____

_____

_____

_____

4 According to an NHS-funded report in *Health Technology Assessment* 2010, about half of the results of all clinical trials are never published. Why does this cast doubt upon the results of some trials that are reported?

_____

_____

_____

_____

_____

Normal distribution

1 The resting heart rate for men is normally distributed with mean 68 and standard deviation 13. Find the probability that a randomly-chosen man has:

(a) a heart rate under 100

_____

_____

(b) an abnormal heart rate outside the range 40–100.

_____

_____

_____

_____

2 Some examinations are graded in terms of the mean μ and standard deviation σ of the marks. For example, the lowest marks for grades A, B, C, D and U in a law examination are as given in the table.

Grade	A	B	C	D	U
Minimum mark	$\mu+2\sigma$	$\mu+\sigma$	$\mu-\sigma$	$\mu-2\sigma$	0

(a) Estimate the proportion of the candidates graded D. State any assumptions you have made.

_____

_____

_____

_____

_____

(b) The law examination was taken by 500 students. Bursaries of $4000 were awarded to each student who achieved grade A. Find the expected cost of these bursaries.

_____

_____

_____

3 The arrival times of a weekday train are normally distributed with mean 8.54am and s.d. 4 minutes. In one year, how often would you expect the train to arrive after 9am?

_____

_____

_____

_____

_____

4 The lengths of 250 mm connecting rods purchased from supplier X have a mean of 250 mm and a standard deviation of 0.4 mm.

(a) A sample of a dozen rods from another supplier have lengths in mm of:

249.4, 250.8, 249.7, 250.4, 249.6, 250.1, 249.8, 249.9, 250.0, 250.2, 250.4, 249.7

Compare these rods with those from supplier X. Would you choose to switch supplier?

_____

_____

_____

In questions of this type, always calculate means and standard deviations so that you can support your statements with numerical calculations.

_____

_____

_____

_____

(b) Any rod with a length l mm outside the interval $249 \leq l \leq 251$ cannot be used. In a batch of 3000 rods from supplier X, how many would you expect to be unusable?

_____

_____

_____

_____

_____

_____

5 Adults with a body mass index (BMI) of over 25 are classified as overweight. In the UK, 61.7% of adults are classified as overweight.

Adults with a BMI of over 30 are classified as obese. In the UK, 24.9% of adults are classified as obese.

(a) A large sample of UK adults suggests that the BMIs of adults in the UK has mean 26.5 and s.d. 5. Check if this sample is consistent with the data given.

Comment on your numerical answers. State any assumptions you have made.

_____

_____

_____

_____

_____

_____

_____

_____

_____

_____

_____

_____

(b) A sample of 10 male patients in a diabetes clinic have the following BMIs:

$$34, 39, 25, 20, 28, 23, 34, 32, 25, 36$$

Compare these patients with the general adult population of the UK. What does your answer suggest?

_____

_____

_____

_____

_____

_____

_____

6 The ideal pH value (a measure of acidity) of the soil is 7.0 when growing artichokes. Acid soil, with a pH value of below 6.5, must be treated with lime, thus increasing the cost of any crop.

Giovanni is considering using some of his land to cultivate artichokes.
The pH values of soil in the first possible field has mean 7 and s.d. 0.3.
In a second field, ten samples of soil have pH values as shown:

$$6.9, 6.6, 7.0, 6.8, 6.8, 6.7, 7.0, 6.8, 7.1, 6.7$$

(a) Compare the two fields in terms of their suitability for growing artichokes.

> In questions of this type, always comment on means and standard deviations in the context of the question, not as abstract numbers.

(b) Calculate what percentage of the first field you would expect to be too acidic for growing artichokes. State any assumptions you have made.

Confidence intervals

1 A random sample of size n is taken from a distribution $N(\mu, \sigma^2)$. Which of the following is the standard error of the mean?

$$\frac{\sigma^2}{n} \qquad \sqrt{\frac{\sigma}{n}} \qquad \frac{\sigma}{n} \qquad \frac{\sigma}{\sqrt{n}}$$

2 The weights of lettuces delivered to a supermarket are normally distributed with mean 600 g and s.d. 25 g.

   (a) What is the probability that the weight of a randomly-chosen lettuce will lie between 590 g and 610 g?

   _____

   _____

   _____

   _____

   _____

   (b) What is the probability that the mean weight of four randomly-chosen lettuces will lie between 590 g and 610 g?

   > First find the standard error of the mean.

   _____

   _____

   _____

   _____

3 The levels of radon gas $(Bq\,m^{-3})$ in six houses in a village are as shown:

$$18.5, \ 19.1, \ 21.7, \ 20.3, \ 18.4, \ 21.4$$

Assuming that the radon levels are normally distributed, with mean μ and s.d. 1.5, construct a 98% confidence interval for μ.

   _____

   _____

   _____

   _____

   _____

   _____

4 The weights of oranges delivered by a supplier have standard deviation 10 g. A sample of a dozen randomly-selected oranges has mean weight 193 g.

Find a 99% confidence interval for the mean weight of the supplier's oranges and comment on the supplier's claim that the mean weight is 200 g.

_____

_____

_____

_____

5 The IQ scores of the adult population of a town have a normal distribution with mean μ and standard deviation 20 points.

The average scores for each of eight married couples are as shown:

$$91, 122, 125, 100, 131, 88, 97, 90$$

A student uses these scores to estimate that the distribution of IQ scores is $N(105.5, 200)$.

(a) Show how the student obtained this result.

_____

_____

_____

(b) What assumptions has the student made?

_____

_____

_____

_____

_____

(c) Comment on the student's assumptions.

_____

_____

_____

_____

Scatter graphs

1   A researcher measures the maximum
    heart rate of men at different ages.
    The scatter graph shows the results.

> Use scatter graphs to answer these questions, but note that other methods are possible – you will use these in later sections.

(a) Draw the line of best fit by eye.

> Plot the mean point first.

_____

(b) Calculate the gradient of your line
       and interpret it in the real context.

_____

_____

_____

_____

_____

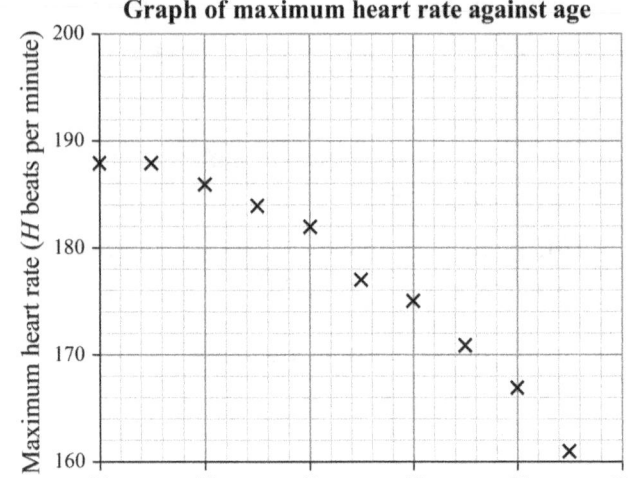

Graph of maximum heart rate against age

(c) (i) Find the equation of your line.

> Substitute the coordinates of a point on your line into $y = mx + c$.

_____

_____

_____

(ii) Why should you not use your equation to predict the maximum heart rate of a 75-year-old man?

_____

_____

(d) The formula $H = 220 - n$ is often used to estimate maximum heart rate.
       Compare the accuracy of this model with your line of best fit.

_____

_____

_____

(e) Comment on the use of a linear model in this context.

_____

_____

Paper 2A activity

2 Three judges in an art competition award marks for ten paintings as shown in the table.

	Painting	A	B	C	D	E	F	G	H	I	J
Mark awarded	**Judge X**	40	46	34	49	49	37	41	36	43	38
	Judge Y	40	39	45	34	35	38	39	43	40	42
	Judge Z	42	42	37	46	45	39	41	37	44	41

After the competition, some of the artists complain about the marks awarded by one of the judges.

You are writing a report for the organisers about this problem.

Use statistical analysis and reasoning to comment on the dispute.

Use correlation to decide which of the judges' marks are out of line with the others.

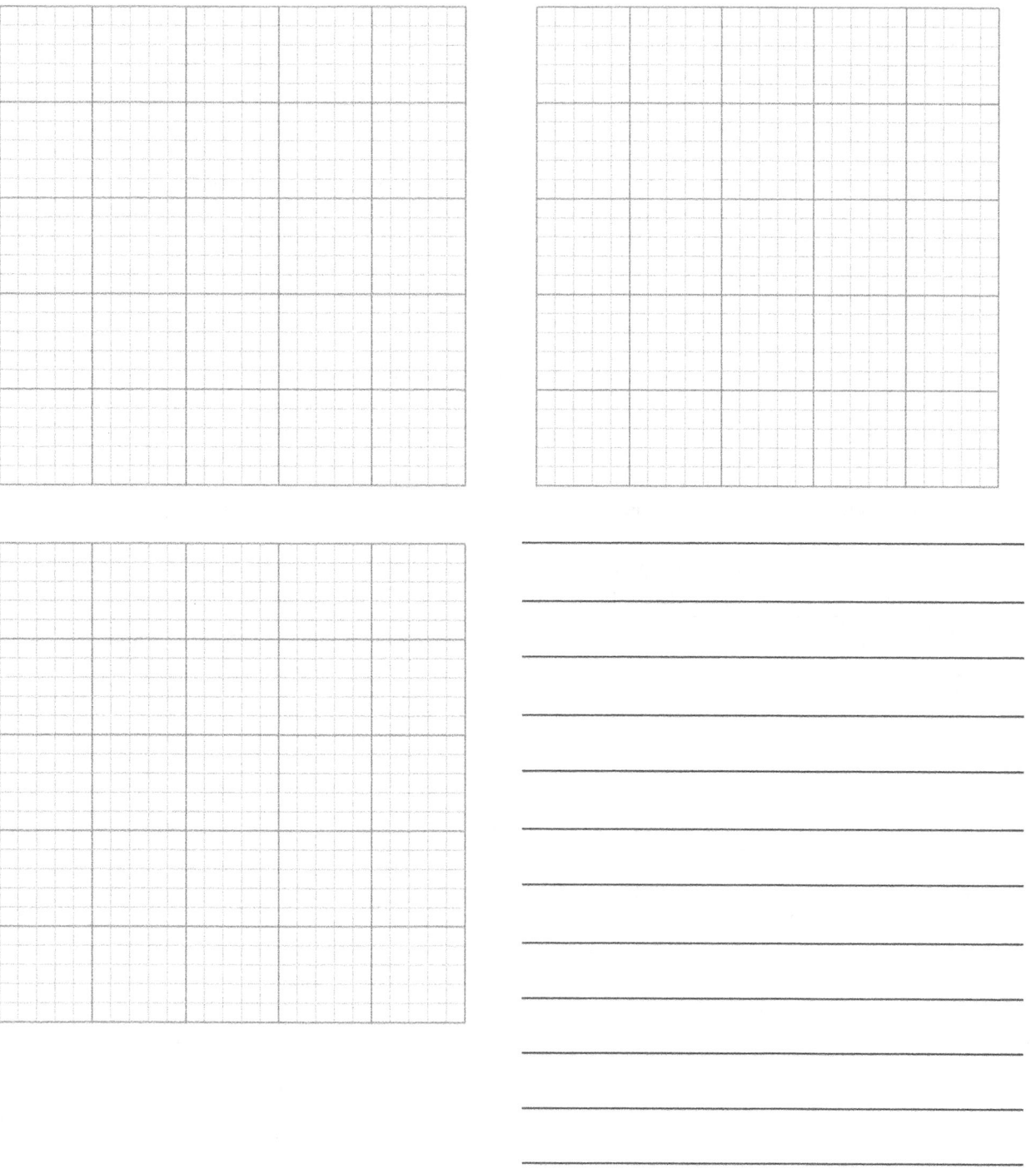

Regression lines

1 The scatter graph from Question **1** on page 38 is shown again here.

   (a) Find the equation of the regression line of maximum heart rate on age.

   Use your calculator.

   _____

   (b) Write down the gradient of the
       regression line.

   _____

   (c) Draw the regression line on the graph.

   _____

   (d) Compare your answers to parts **(a)–(c)**
       with those you gave on page 38.

   _____

   _____

   _____

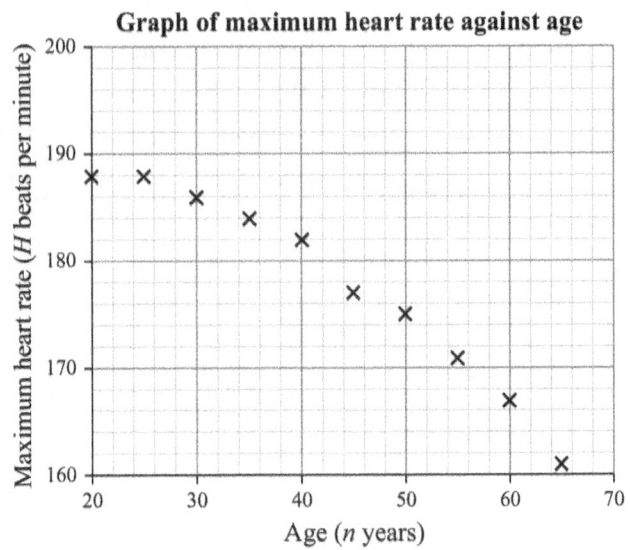

Graph of maximum heart rate against age

2 The table and graph show the funding given to sports that won medals in the 2016 Olympics.

Sport	Funding £m	Number of medals
Athletics	26.8	7
Badminton	5.7	1
Boxing	13.8	3
Canoeing	20.0	4
Cycling	30.3	12
Diving	6.5	3
Equestrian	18.0	3
Gymnastics	14.6	7
Hockey	16.1	1
Judo	7.4	1
Rowing	32.6	5
Sailing	25.5	3
Shooting	3.9	2
Swimming	20.8	6
Taekwando	8.1	3
Triathlon	7.5	3

Source: www.uksport.gov.uk

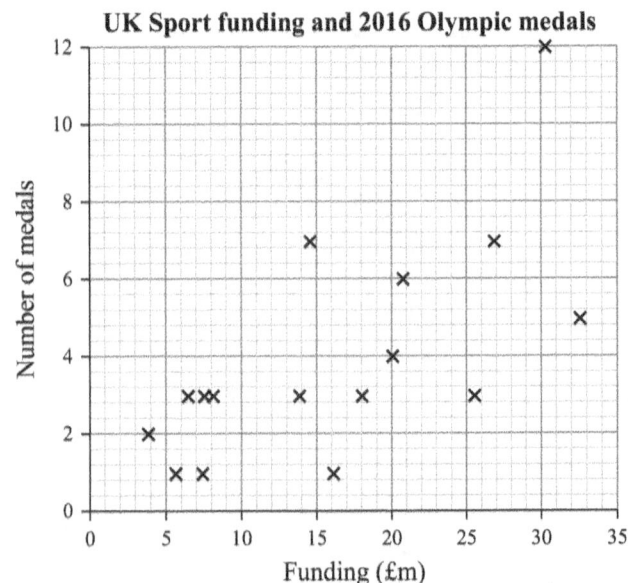

UK Sport funding and 2016 Olympic medals

   (a) Draw the regression line of number of medals on funding.

Paper 2A activity

(b) A sports magazine says that each extra medal costs the country about £5 million.
Comment on this statement.

> Where did this figure come from?
> Is this a correct interpretation?

_____

_____

3 The table gives the employment rate
and average weekly earnings in regions
of the UK in 2016.

  (a) On the grid below, plot a scatter graph
  and draw the regression line of average
  weekly earnings on employment rate.

  (b) Which of the regions is represented by the
  point that is furthest from the regression
  line?

_____

_____

_____

Region	Employment rate (x%)	Average weekly FT earnings (£y)
North East	71.1	492
North West	72.2	502
Yorkshire & The Humber	73.0	498
East Midlands	75.1	502
West Midlands	73.4	508
East	77.1	569
London	73.6	632
South East	78.0	582
South West	77.0	513

Source: ONS

  (c) (i) Find the equation of the regression line
  when this point is omitted.

_____

_____

_____

_____

  (ii) In what ways would the line differ from
  that shown on your graph?

_____

  (d) Comment on your findings.

> Remember to answer this part
> in context.

_____

_____

_____

_____

Applications of the product moment correlation coefficient (pmcc)

1 Question **2** from the scatter graphs section on page 39 is given again here. This time, use product moment correlation coefficients to answer the question.

> This shows that there are often alternative methods that you can use.

Three judges in an art competition award marks for ten paintings as shown.

	Painting	A	B	C	D	E	F	G	H	I	J
Mark awarded	**Judge X**	40	46	34	49	49	37	41	36	43	38
	Judge Y	40	39	45	34	35	38	39	43	40	42
	Judge Z	42	42	37	46	45	39	41	37	44	41

After the competition, some of the artists complain about the marks awarded by one of the judges.

You are writing a report for the organisers about this problem. Use statistical analysis and reasoning to comment on the dispute.

> Use your calculator to work out pmcc values, then consider their signs.

2 Glucose levels after an insulin resistance test are important in the diagnosis of diabetes. However, much simpler measures are often used in clinical tests of risk.

The table gives the results from a sample of 10 male patients in a clinic.

Use statistical analyses and reasoning to decide whether body mass index (BMI) or waist measurements give better indications of high glucose levels.

Patient	Glucose (mg/dl)	BMI (kg/m²)	Waist (cm)
A	121	34	83
B	213	39	101
C	144	25	86
D	162	20	99
E	197	28	102
F	129	23	91
G	175	34	96
H	138	32	84
I	186	25	94
J	150	36	91

3 Use the data from Question **3** of the regression lines section on page 41 to answer this question.

(a) Find the product moment correlation coefficient when London is:

  (i) included _____ **(ii)** excluded _____

(b) Comment on your answers.

_____

_____

_____

4 The table shows the life expectancy of men and women in countries that have joined the European Union since 2000 and the percentage of Gross Domestic Product (GDP) that these countries spend on health.

Country	% of GDP spent on health	Life expectancy (years)	
		Men	Women
Bulgaria	8.4	72	79
Croatia	7.8	75	80
Cyprus	7.4	78	82
Czech Republic	7.4	75	81
Estonia	6.4	73	82
Hungary	7.4	73	79
Latvia	5.9	70	79
Lithuania	6.6	69	80
Malta	9.7	80	84
Poland	6.4	73	81
Romania	5.6	72	79
Slovakia	8.1	73	80
Slovenia	9.2	77	84

(a) Find:

  (i) the regression equation of male life expectancy on % GDP spent on health

  _____

  (ii) the product moment correlation coefficient

  _____

(b) Interpret the gradient of the regression line and the pmcc in terms of the real context.

_____

_____

_____

_____

(c) Find:

  (i) the regression equation of female life expectancy on % GDP spent on health

  _____

  (ii) the product moment correlation coefficient.

  _____

  (iii) Compare your answers with those found in part **(a)** and interpret the results in the real context.

  _____

  _____

  _____

Critical path analysis

1 The precedence table for a project is as shown.

Activity	Duration (weeks)	Immediate predecessors
A	2	–
B	3	A
C	4	A
D	6	A
E	3	B, C
F	2	D
G	3	B, E
H	1	E
I	1	E, F
J	3	G, H, I

(a) Draw an activity diagram for this project.

Your entire answer depends upon an accurate and legible diagram.

(b) Complete the early and late times for each activity.

_____

_____

(c) List the critical activities.

_____

_____

(d) Draw a Gantt chart for this project.

(The critical activities can be put on one row.)

Weeks

(e) How can the activities be arranged so that activity I occurs at the same time as only one other activity?

_____

_____

_____

(f) Activities D and H each take 2 weeks longer to complete than expected. What is the effect on the total time of the project? Justify your answer.

> Use floats to justify answers about delays.

_____

_____

_____

_____

Venn diagrams

1 The Venn diagram shows the number of students choosing some of the optional activities during one week at an outdoor centre. There were 34 students in total.

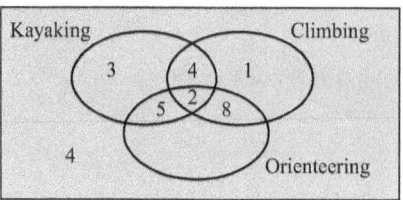

(a) Fill in the missing number on the diagram.

(b) What is the probability that a student took part in the kayaking?

_____

_____

(c) What is the probability that a student who took part in the kayaking also took part in climbing?

_____

_____

(d) Find the probability that a student took part in orienteering given that they had taken part in kayaking.

> This is the same type of question as part (c) but asked in a different way.

_____

_____

(e) Find the mean number of these activities taken by the students.

_____

_____

_____

(f) In a season, approximately 200 students take a holiday at the centre. How many of these would you expect to choose kayaking as an activity? State any assumptions you have made.

_____

_____

_____

Paper 2B activity

2 There are 47 member states of the Council of Europe. The Venn diagram shows how many are islands, how many are in the Schengen area and how many are in the EU.

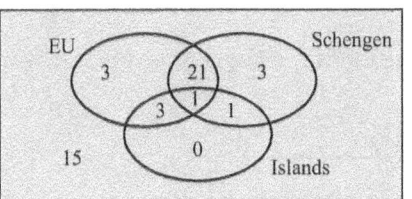

Council of Europe

(a) If one of the member states is chosen at random, what is the probability it is an island?

_____

_____

(b) What is the probability that one of the island states, chosen at random, is

(i) in the EU?

_____

_____

(ii) in the Schengen area?

_____

_____

(c) Alessa argues that:

'Precisely one of the 47 states is an island, in the EU and in the Schengen area. Therefore a citizen of a state in the Council of Europe has probability roughly 2% of being from an island state that is both in the EU and in the Schengen area.'

Use the internet (if necessary) to find which island state is both in the EU and in the Schengen area. What is wrong with Alessa's argument?

_____

_____

_____

_____

_____

_____

_____

Tree diagrams

1   The contingency table shows the total student numbers at Oxford University.

	Men	Women	Total
Undergraduates	6131	5472	11603
Graduates	5909	4590	10499
Other	201	299	500
Total	12241	10361	22602

Source: www.ox.ac.uk (Dec 2015)

For an Oxford University student chosen at random, calculate and insert the probabilities on the branches of this tree diagram.

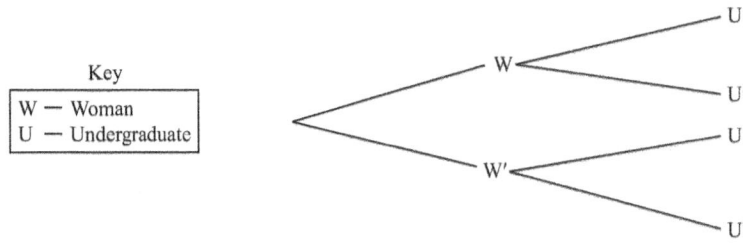

Key

| W — Woman |
| U — Undergraduate |

2   Two runners in a race have chances of $\dfrac{1}{3}$ and $\dfrac{1}{5}$ respectively, of breaking the current record.

(a)   Making any necessary assumptions, draw a tree diagram to represent this situation.

(b)   What is the probability that the record is broken by at least one of the runners?

_____

_____

(c)   What assumption did you make? Do you think your assumption is realistic?

_____

_____

_____

_____

3 Consider three types of pea plant, P, H and W. When two plants are cross-pollinated, the probabilities for the new plant's type are shown in the table.

	{P,P}	{P,H}	{P,W}	{H,H}	{H,W}	{W,W}
P	1	0.5	0	0.25	0	0
H	0	0.5	1	0.5	0.5	0
W	0	0	0	0.25	0.5	1

So, for example, {P,P} represents both original plants being of type P. In that case, the new plant is certain to be of type P.

(a) Complete this tree diagram for cross-pollinating a type H plant with a plant chosen at random from a set of plants with P, H and W plants in the ratio 1:2:1.

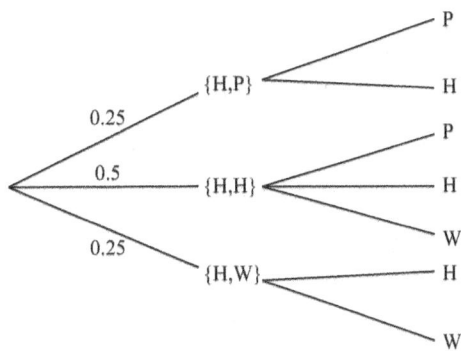

(b) Find the ratio of P, H and W plants that are produced by the cross-pollination of part **(a)**.

_____

_____

(c) In a famous experiment, the scientist Gregor Mendel cross-pollinated type P plants (which had purple flowers) with type W plants (which had white flowers). Perhaps surprisingly, the plants that this produced **all** had purple flowers. The next surprise was that propagating from these new plants then produced plants which had purple and white flowers in the ratio 3:1. Briefly explain this using the information in this question.

_____

_____

_____

_____

_____

Control measures

1   A contractor will incur a £20 000 penalty on a project if either or both of two critical activities (x and y) are delayed. Each has probability 0.2 of being delayed.

   (a) Complete the tree diagram.

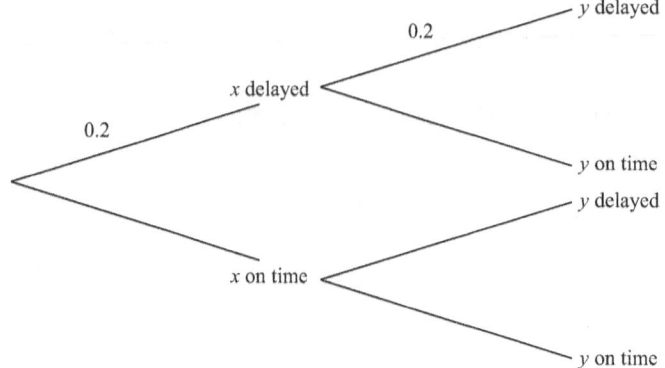

Probability =   0.04

Probability = _____

Probability = _____

Probability = _____

   (b) Work out the expected penalty.

   _____

   _____

   _____

   _____

   _____

   _____

   (c) State an assumption you have made in answering Question **1 (a)** and **(b)**.

   _____

   _____

   _____

   (d) Why might the contractor be willing to pay slightly more than the expected penalty to prevent a delay?

   _____

   _____

   _____

   _____

2 The contractor can employ more workers to ensure that either or both of x and y are completed on time. The costs of these options are shown in the table.

(a) Complete the table.

Extra workers	Extra cost	Probability of delay	Expected penalty
For x only	£6000	0.2	
For y only	£2000	0.2	
For both x and y	£7000	0	£0

(b) Give a possible reason why the cost of extra workers for both x and y is less than the sum of the two individual costs.

_____

_____

_____

_____

(c) The contractor has a total of four options (including the option of not employing any extra workers). Make a recommendation to the contractor as to which option to choose. Fully justify your recommendation.

> You must justify your recommendation with appropriate calculations.

_____

_____

_____

_____

_____

_____

_____

_____

_____

_____

_____

Conditional probability

1   A test for a particular disease correctly indicates its presence 95% of the time and correctly indicates its absence 99% of the time.

The disease affects 1% of the population.

> Many students find that using a tree diagram helps them solve questions on conditional probability.

(a) Use the multiplication law to find the probability that a randomly-chosen person will have the disease and that it will be correctly indicated by the test.

> Writing out an answer in a way that others will understand is much easier if you let D be the event of having the disease and T be the event of the test indicating the disease.

_____

_____

_____

(b) Use the multiplication law to find the probability that a randomly-chosen person will not have the disease but that it will be incorrectly indicated by the test.

_____

_____

_____

(c) Use your answers to parts (a) and (b) to find the probability that the test will indicate the disease in a randomly-chosen person.

_____

_____

_____

(d) Use the multiplication law to find the probability that a randomly-chosen person has the disease given that it has been indicated by the test.

> This question is asking for $P(D|T)$.

_____

_____

_____

(e) In a large testing programme, there are 51 people for whom the test has indicated the presence of the disease. How many are likely to have the disease?

_____

_____

2 A test for a particular disease always correctly indicates its presence and correctly indicates its absence 99% of the time.

The disease affects 0.01% of the population.

A person is indicated as having the disease by this test. How worried should they be?

> Remember, you **must** give calculations to justify your answer.

_____

_____

_____

_____

_____

_____

_____

_____

3 Louise's mother has a rare gene which has probability of 0.5 of being passed from parent to child.

   (a) If Louise has a child, what is the probability it will have the gene?

_____

_____

   (b) If Louise has a child, what is the probability it will not have the gene?

_____

_____

   (c) Given that Louise's first child does not have the gene, what is the probability Louise has the gene?

> Let L be the event of Louise having the gene and C be the event of her child having the gene. This question is asking for $P(L|C')$

_____

_____

_____

_____

_____

Expectation

1

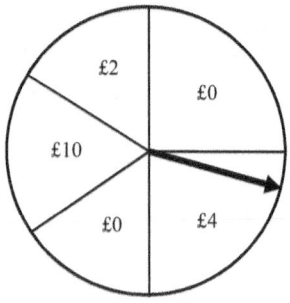

In a game of chance, the spinner stops in one of the regions. You can assume that the spinner is not biased and so, for example, it has probability $\frac{1}{6}$ of stopping in the £2 region.

A player wins the amount shown in the region where the spinner has stopped. What is a fair price to pay to play this game?

_____

_____

_____

_____

_____

2 The prize structure for the Health Lottery is shown in the table.

Numbers matched	Prize	Odds of winning
Match 5	£100 000*	1 in 2 118 760
Match 4 + Bonus Ball	£10 000	1 in 423 752
Match 4	£250	1 in 9631
Match 3 + Bonus Ball	£50	1 in 4815
Match 3	£20	1 in 224
Match 2 + Bonus Ball	£10	1 in 224

This prize can be less than £100 000

What are the expected annual winnings for someone who buys a £1 ticket each week? State any assumptions you have made.

_____

_____

_____

_____

Paper 2B activity

3 A motorist's route to work involves passing through two potential bottlenecks. On a particular trip, the probabilities of being delayed are independently 0.3 and 0.6

(a) Find the probabilities of there being

    (i)   no delays _____

    (ii) 1 delay   _____

    (iii) 2 delays.   _____

(b) What is the expected probability of delays?

_____

_____

4 A company sells tickets to tourists for a day's sightseeing at £50 per person. This cost is non-refundable but experience shows that there is a probability of 3% that any individual tourist will not turn up on the day.

There are 30 places on the tour. If the tour company overbooks and cannot provide a paid customer with a place, then that customer will receive their payment back and £50 compensation.

(a) If the company sells 31 tickets for a tour, what is the probability that not all of the customers will turn up?

> First find the probability that they **will** all show up.

_____

_____

(b) Comment on any assumptions you have made in answering part (a).

_____

_____

_____

(c) What is the expected extra profit from selling 31 tickets rather than 30 tickets?

_____

_____

_____

(d) Would you recommend selling 31 tickets?

_____

_____

_____

Insurance

1   Ron makes a profit of 20% on each liqueur he produces and sells. He is intending to book a 6 m × 12 m trade stall at a county show. A standard site costs £605 and there is a 40% surcharge for a premium site on Main Drive. From past experience, Ron expects his sales at the show to be as shown in the table.

Expected sales	Good weather	Rain
Standard site	£5000	£2000
Premium site	£6000	£3000

According to Met Office forecasts there is a 29% probability of rain on the days of the show.

(a) At which type of site should Ron expect to make the greater profit?

> You **must** give calculations to justify your advice.

_____

_____

_____

_____

_____

_____

_____

_____

(b) Ron realises that he will make a loss if it rains. However, for an extra fee of £100, the event organisers will refund half of the standard site fee if it rains. Should Ron pay this fee?

> Apply the cost-benefit principle. Compare the expected **extra** benefits and the **extra** cost.

_____

_____

_____

_____

_____

_____

2

> Your chosen tickets are only valid on the trains you've selected and are non-refundable.
>
> **Add Cancellation Protection**   ⭘ **Only £4**
>
>   ⊗ No thanks

(a) You intend to buy an Advance single ticket for £37.50 but realise that if you have to cancel your journey due to unforeseen circumstances you will not be able to get your money back. Should you pay the extra £4 to cover you against this eventuality?

> Consider different probabilities or a general probability p.

Analyse this situation in terms of the likelihood that a person would need to cancel the journey.

_____

_____

_____

_____

_____

_____

_____

_____

(b) You read the small print of the policy and realise that to claim a refund you will have to pay a processing fee of £10 and, for an unexpected illness, you will need to provide a doctor's note which will cost £20.

How does this information affect your analysis in part **(a)**?

_____

_____

_____

_____

_____

_____

_____

_____

_____

Intersection points

1   The fastest land animal is the cheetah, which can run at $27\,\mathrm{m\,s^{-1}}$ in short bursts.

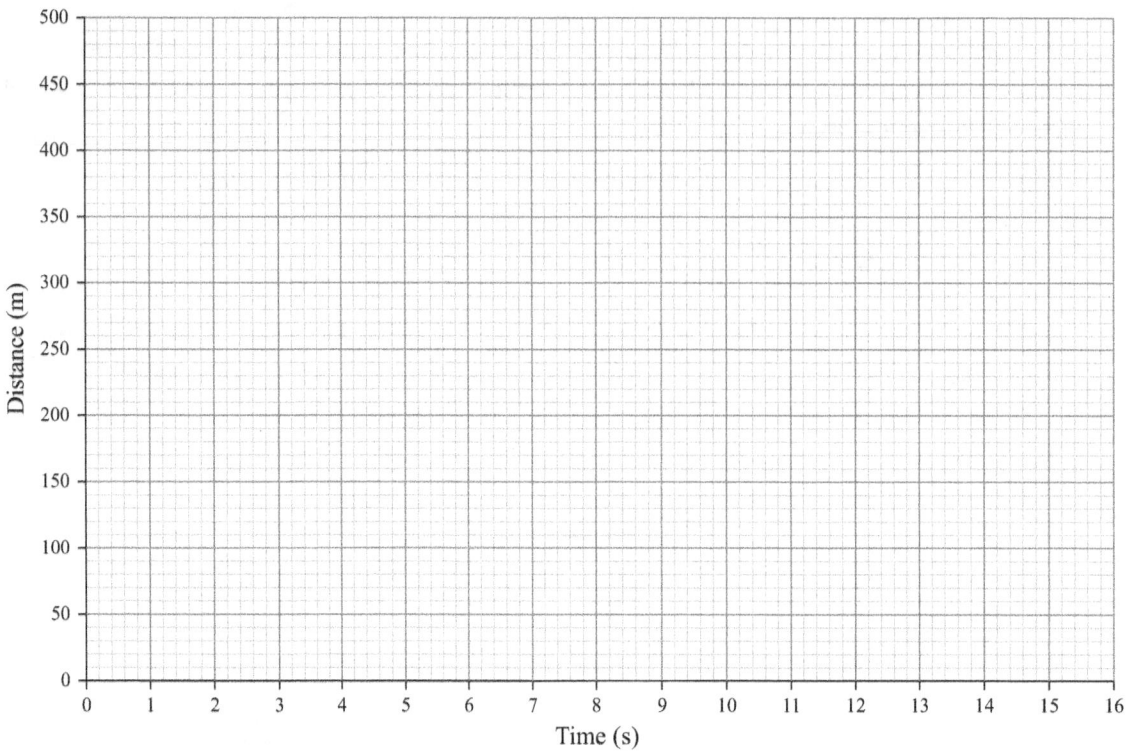

(a) On the graph, represent the motion of a cheetah that starts at distance 0 and runs at a constant speed of $27\,\mathrm{m\,s^{-1}}$ for 400 m before being forced to rest.

(b) A gazelle is at rest, 100 m in front of the cheetah, when it realises the danger and accelerates to its top speed of $21\,\mathrm{m\,s^{-1}}$ in 3 seconds. Find how far the gazelle travels in this time. State any assumptions you have made.

_____

_____

_____

(c) On the above graph, represent the motion of the gazelle. Assume it starts at distance 100 m and that it runs at a constant speed of $21\,\mathrm{m\,s^{-1}}$ after the first 3 seconds.

(d) When will the gazelle be caught?

_____

(e) By drawing a line on the above graph, or otherwise, find how far from the cheetah the gazelle would have needed to be initially, in order to escape.

_____

2 The table shows a comparison between the standard rates of three energy suppliers.

Supplier	Annual standing charge	Cost per kwh	Representative cost for 1200 kwh
British Gas	£90.41	11.620p	229.85
EDF Energy	£65.70	12.950p	221.10
First Utility	£17.37	18.170p	235.41

Source: uSwitch 15 Nov 2016

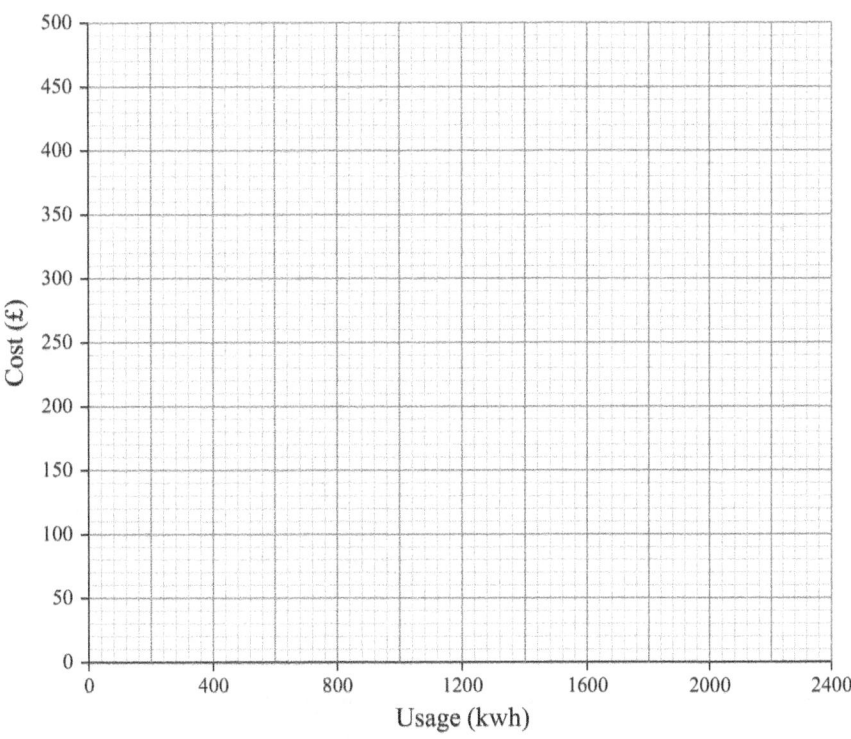

(a) Draw and label lines on the graph to represent the three tariffs.

(b) Explain why it is clear from the data in the table that First Utility is the best choice for a consumer with a low annual consumption of electricity.

_____

_____

(c) Use your answer to part **(a)** to give a precise description of how a consumer should decide between the three companies.

_____

_____

_____

_____

_____

_____

Gradients

1 The graph shows the number of suspected cases of Ebola in Sierra Leone during the 2014 West African Ebola outbreak. The time, t, refers to the number of months after March 2014.

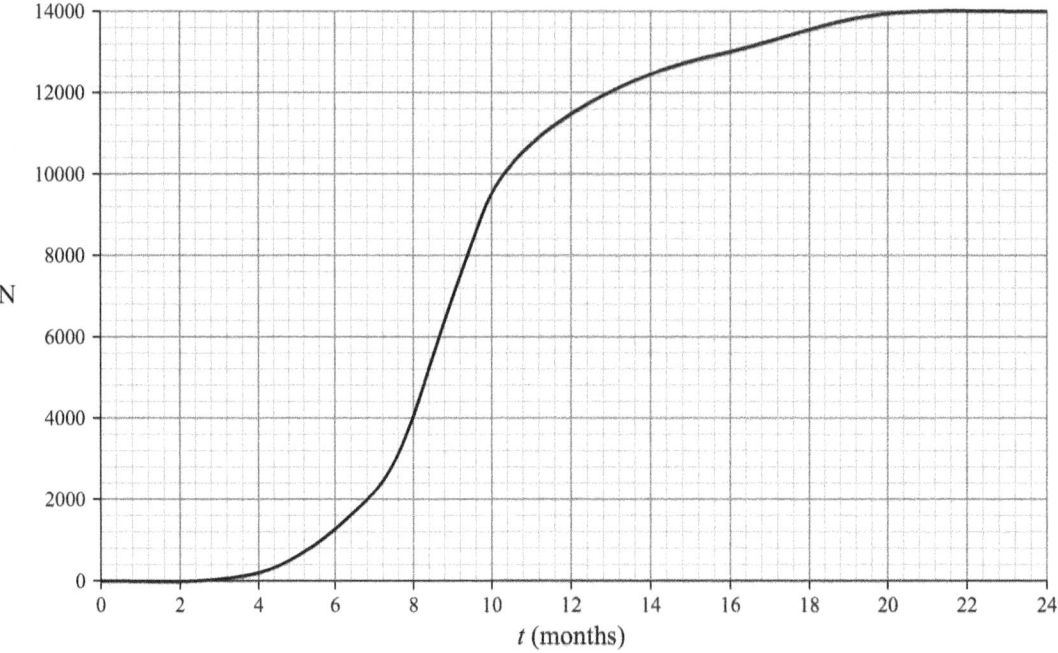

Source: WHO Situation Report (April 2016)

(a) By drawing a suitable line on the graph above, find the maximum gradient of the curve.

(b) Interpret your answer to part (a) in context.

Use actual dates

_____

_____

_____

_____

(c) On the graph, plot the Verhulst logistic curve

$$N = \frac{14000}{1+1200(2.2)^{-t}}$$

How well does this model the outbreak?

_____

_____

_____

Paper 2C activity

2 The total monthly costs of a poussin farmer depend upon the number reared.

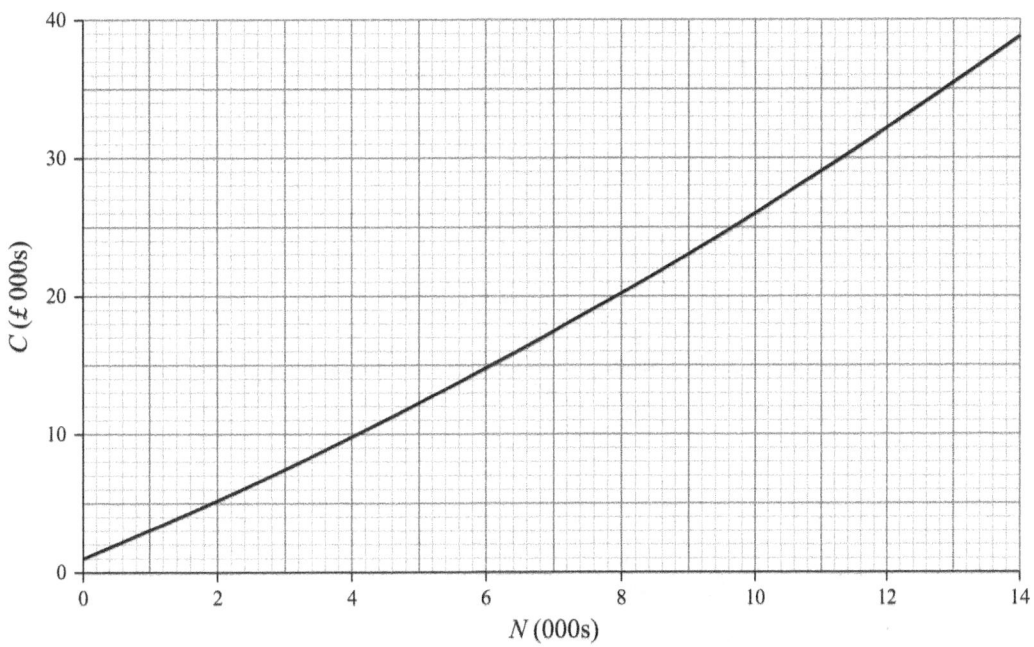

(a) By drawing a suitable line on the graph, find the gradient of the curve at the point where 12 000 poussins are being reared.

_____

_____

(b) Interpret your answer to part **(a)** in context.

_____

_____

_____

(c) Currently, the farmer is rearing 10 000 poussins per month and there is a market demand for poussin at a price of £3.20 per bird. Use your answer to part **(b)** to give a reasoned recommendation as to whether or not the farmer should increase production.

_____

_____

_____

_____

_____

Velocity-time graphs

1 Typical velocity–time graphs for arrows released from *traditional* bows and from *compound* bows are shown in the graph.

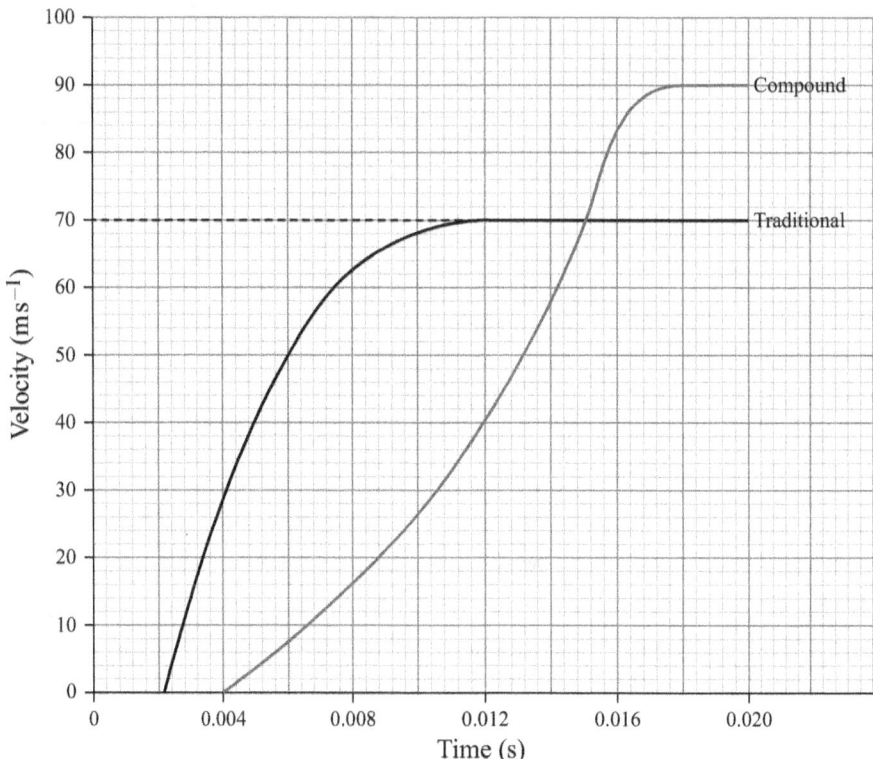

(a) What is the maximum velocity of the arrow from the traditional bow?

> Read questions carefully. 'Traditional' is a crucial word in part **(a)**.

_____

_____

(b) Explain how the graph shows that this arrow leaves the bow after approximately 12 milliseconds.

_____

_____

_____

_____

(c) By drawing a suitable line on the graph, find the maximum acceleration of this arrow.

_____

2 (a) Using the graph in Question **1**, compare the velocities of arrows from the traditional and compound bows during the first 20 milliseconds from release.

_____

_____

_____

_____

(b) Compare the accelerations of arrows from the traditional and compound bows during the first 20 milliseconds from release.

_____

_____

_____

_____

(c) Assume that arrows are released from a traditional and a compound bow at the same time. How can you tell from the graph that the arrow from the traditional bow has travelled further after 20 milliseconds?

_____

_____

_____

_____

(d) Estimate how far the arrow from the traditional bow has travelled in the first 20 milliseconds. You must show your working.

_____

_____

_____

_____

_____

Exponential functions

1 *E. coli* is an extensively studied bacterium commonly found in the intestines of humans and other mammals.

Under favourable conditions, at time t minutes, the number of *E. coli* bacteria in a colony is given by

$$500e^{0.0347t}$$

(a) Calculate how many bacteria there are in the colony after 1 hour.

_____

_____

(b) How long does it take for the number of bacteria to reach 1 million?

_____

_____

_____

(c) Show that the number of bacteria doubles every 20 minutes.

> You must show this in general.
> Use time $t + 20$.

_____

_____

_____

_____

2 A farmer is building up his flock of sheep. His ewes are able to give birth when they are 1 year old and have two lambs a year on average.

(a) Explain why the farmer can expect his number of ewes to double every year. State any assumptions you have made.

_____

_____

_____

_____

(b) His flock initially has 50 ewes. Deduce a formula for the expected number of ewes after n years.

_____

_____

Paper 2C activity

3 The height, h metres, of a tree is predicted to be given by

$$h = 100 - 99e^{-0.00306t}$$

where t is the number of years since its planting in 2009.

(a) How tall was the tree when it was planted?

_____

_____

(b) When is the tree expected to reach a height of 50 m?

_____

_____

_____

4 The amount of a radioactive substance remaining after t years is given by

$$N_0 e^{-kt}$$

where N_0 is the initial amount and k is a positive constant.

Given that 10% of the substance has decayed after 1 year, find its half-life, i.e. the time it takes for half the substance to decay.

_____

_____

_____

_____

_____

5 What is the gradient of the graph of $y = e^x$ at the point where $x = 10$? Explain your answer.

_____

_____

_____

_____

_____

_____

Fitting quadratics

1

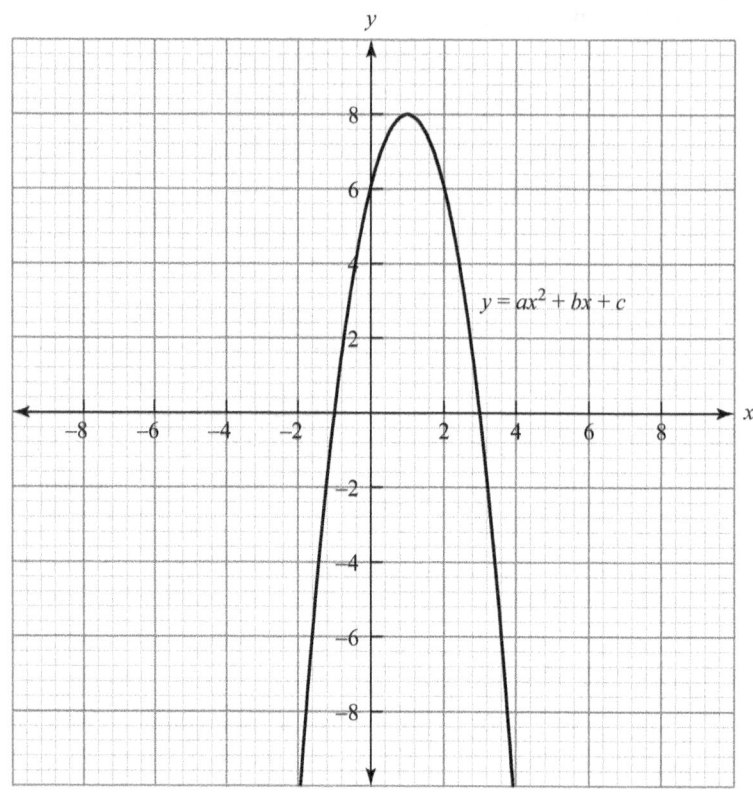

$$y = ax^2 + bx + c$$

(a) Complete this list of equations for $a, b,$ and c obtained by using each of the four known points in turn.

$(-1, 0)$ $0 = a - b + c$

$\boxed{\text{Put } x = -1 \text{ and } y = 0.}$

$(0, 6)$ _____

$(1, 8)$ _____

$(3, 0)$ _____

(b) Find c by using the simplest of the equations from part **(a)**.

$\boxed{\text{Use the simplest equations whenever possible.}}$

_____

(c) Solve two of the other equations from part **(a)** simultaneously to find a and b.

_____

_____

(d) Write down the equation of the curve.

_____

_____

Paper 2C activity

2 Demelza's new business makes a profit of £5000 in its second year and £17 000 in its third year.

She models the profit £P in the xth year by the equation $P = a(x^2 - x) + c$.

(a) What two points on the graph of P against x does she know?

_____

(b) Use the two points from part **(a)** to find the values of a and c.

_____

_____

_____

_____

_____

(c) What does Demelza's model suggest happened in the first year of the business's operation?

_____

_____

3 The total profit, £P, from the sales of an article at a selling price of £s per article is modelled by the quadratic equation $P = a - b(s - 50)^2$.

At a selling price of £70, the profit is £40 000.

At a selling price of £40, the profit is £100 000.

(a) Find a and b.

_____

_____

_____

_____

_____

(b) What selling price would you recommend? Give a reason for your answer.

_____

_____

_____

Fitting exponentials

1 The cooling curve for a liquid is shown on the graph. An exponential equation of the form

$$T = A + Be^{-kt}$$

is to be fitted to the curve.

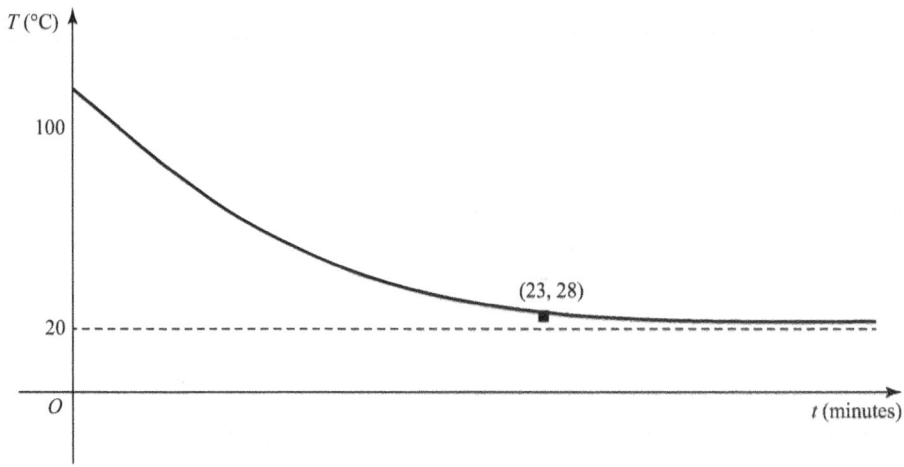

(a) Find A by considering large values of t.

> As t becomes large $e^{-kt} \to 0$

_____

_____

(b) Find B by putting $t = 0$.

_____

_____

(c) Substitute $t = 23$ and $T = 28$ to obtain an equation for k.

> Remember to use your values for A and B.

_____

_____

(d) Solve the equation for k.

_____

_____

_____

_____

_____

2 Find the equation of this curve in the form $y = A + Be^{-kx}$

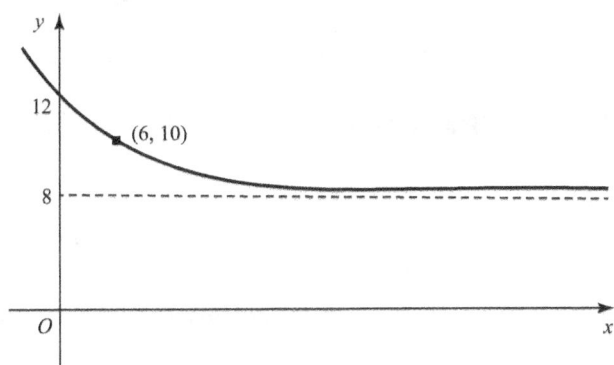

_____

_____

_____

3 Match up these equations with their graphs.

$y = e^{2x} - 5$ $\qquad$ $y = 8 - e^{5x}$ $\qquad$ $y = 3 - 5e^{-7x}$ $\qquad$ $y = 3e^{-x} - 2$

(a) $y =$ _____

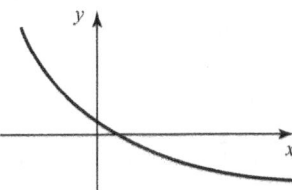

(b) $y =$ _____

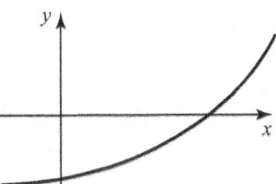

(c) $y =$ _____

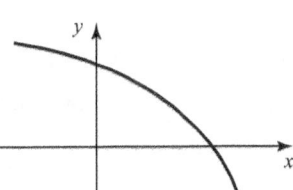

(d) $y =$ _____

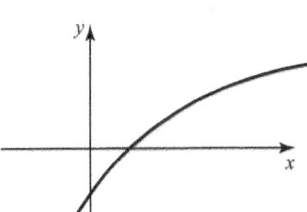

Preliminary material (general)

The material on this page relates to the questions on Taxation on pages 20–21 and page 110.

Income Tax and National Insurance 2016–2017

Income Tax 2016–2017

Everyone in the UK has a personal allowance. This is their annual amount of tax-free income. The standard personal allowance for 2016–2017 was £11 000.

The rates of income tax you pay depend on how much **taxable income** you have above your personal allowance.

Income tax rates and bands 2016–2017

Rate	Taxable income
Basic: 20%	£0–£32 000
Higher: 40%	£32 001–£150 000
Additional: 45%	Over £150 000

To calculate your income tax if your annual income is £100 000 or less

Find your taxable income by subtracting your personal allowance from your annual gross income.

You pay income tax at 20% on the first £32 000 of your taxable income.

You pay income tax at 40% on your taxable income over £32 000.

National Insurance (NI) 2016–2017

Percentage NI Due	Minimum Weekly Income	Maximum Weekly Income	Minimum Monthly Income	Maximum Monthly Income	Minimum Yearly Income	Maximum Yearly Income
Nil		below £112		below £486		below £5832
0%	£112	£155	£486	£672	£5832	£8064
12%	£155.01	£827	£672.01	£3583	£8064.01	£42 996
2%	above £827		above £3583		above £42 996	

Examples

A person who had a weekly income of £350 paid 12% on the amount above £155.

A person who had a weekly income of £950 paid 12% on the amount between £155.01 and £827 plus 2% of the amount above £827.

Gross and net pay

Your net pay (or take-home pay) is the amount of money you receive after income tax, national insurance and other deductions have been taken off your gross pay (your wage or salary).

This is a practice paper so the wording on this cover page will not be *exactly* the same as on a real exam paper.

Level 3 Certificate
MATHEMATICAL STUDIES

Set 1, Paper 1

Name: _____

Class: _____

Date: _____   **Time allowed:** 1 hour 30 minutes

Materials

For this paper you must have:

- a clean copy of the Preliminary material
- a scientific calculator or a graphics calculator
- a copy of the formulae sheet
- a ruler.

Instructions

- Use black ink or black ball-point pen. Draw diagrams in pencil.
- Fill in your name, class and the date at the top of this page.
- Answer all the questions.
- Do all rough work on this paper. Cross through any work that you do not want to be marked.
- In all calculations, show clearly how you work out your answer.
- The final answer to questions should be given to an appropriate degree of accuracy.
- You may not refer to the copy of the Preliminary material that was available prior to this examination. A clean copy is enclosed for your use.

Information

- The maximum mark for this paper is 60.
- The marks for each question are shown in brackets [ ].
- Use this as a guide as to how much time to spend on each question.

Advice

- Read each question carefully before you start to answer it.
- Keep an eye on the time.
- Try to answer every question.
- Check your answers if you have time at the end.

Preliminary material instructions

- The preliminary material will be given to you before your exam.
- You must not take annotated preliminary materials into the exam.
- You will be given a clean copy by your teacher.

Question	Mark
1a	
1b	
1c	
1d	
2a	
2b	
2c	
3	
4	
5a	
5b	
6a	
6b	
6c	
6d	
7	
Total	

Speeding

A reduction in average speeds of just 1 mph would reduce the frequency of accidents by approximately:

- 6% on roads with low average speeds
- 4% on medium-speed roads
- 3% on the higher-speed main roads.

Driving at Work: Managing Work Related Road Safety, HSE & Department for Transport, 2014

When a car skids to a stop, the length of the skid depends upon many factors, including:

- the car's initial speed
- the weather conditions
- the road surface
- the condition of the tyres.

By making allowance for the other factors, police accident investigators can use the lengths of skids to help determine the speed of cars involved in accidents.

1   The estimated numbers of African and Asian elephants are 600 000 and 60 000, respectively. One area of interest in elephant behaviour concerns their sleeping patterns.

(a) Circle the words that describe data about the length of time an elephant spends asleep.

    discrete   qualitative   continuous   quantitative   **[2 marks]**

(b) For a sample of 100 elephants, stratified by continent, Samuel chose 91 African elephants and nine Asian elephants. Show why he used these numbers.

           [2 marks]

_____

_____

_____

_____

(c) For the sample of Asian elephants, Samuel chose some elephants in a local zoo. Describe one advantage and one disadvantage of choosing the sample in this manner.

           [2 marks]

_____

_____

_____

_____

_____

(d) Describe how random numbers could be used to choose nine Asian elephants from those in the zoo.

           [3 marks]

_____

_____

_____

_____

_____

_____

_____

2 When Fiona leaves university, she has a student loan of £30 000. After her first year of working, on a gross salary of £41 000 per year, the loan has incurred interest of 4.6% and she has repaid 9% of what she has earned over the threshold of £21 000 per year.

(a) How much does Fiona owe after this first year of working?

[3 marks]

_____

_____

_____

_____

_____

_____

(b) Fiona assumes that both her salary and the interest rate will stay the same. Describe roughly what Fiona will find if she repeats the calculation in part (a) for subsequent years.

[3 marks]

_____

_____

_____

_____

_____

_____

_____

_____

_____

(c) Explain why Fiona's student loan would not add to her financial difficulties if she lost her job.

[1 mark]

_____

_____

_____

_____

_____

3 The percentages of the population of Egypt in different age bands are shown in the table.

Age	0–9	10–19	20–29	30–39	40–49	50–59	60–69	70+
%	21.8	19.1	20.0	13.8	10.4	8.0	4.4	2.5

The age distributions of the UK are illustrated by this box and whisker plot.

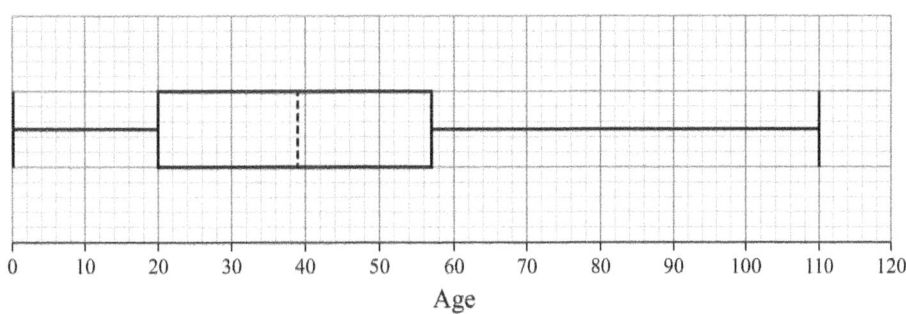

Age

Contrast the age distributions of Egypt and the UK, supporting your comparison with numerical evidence. Suggest reasons for the major differences.

[7 marks]

_____

_____

_____

_____

_____

_____

_____

_____

_____

_____

_____

_____

_____

_____

_____

_____

4 A small meteorite reaches the surface of the Earth. Estimate the probability that this meteorite will hit you.

State any assumptions you have made.

You must show working to justify your answer.

[7 marks]

_____

_____

_____

_____

_____

_____

_____

_____

_____

_____

_____

_____

_____

_____

_____

_____

_____

_____

_____

_____

_____

_____

_____

5 Use **Income Tax and National Insurance 2016–2017** on page 70.

During the year 2016–2017, Neil had an annual salary of £45 000.

His personal tax allowance was £11 000.

(a) Find his monthly take-home pay.

[6 marks]

_____

_____

_____

_____

_____

_____

_____

_____

_____

_____

_____

_____

(b) Julie's annual salary was £5000 more than Neil's. What was the difference in their monthly take-home pay? State any assumptions you have made.

[4 marks]

_____

_____

_____

_____

_____

_____

_____

_____

_____

_____

6   A Financial Conduct Authority (FCA) rule means that the interest on short-term loans cannot exceed 0.8% per day of the amount borrowed.

(a) If you borrow £100 for 13 days, show that £10.40 is the maximum amount of interest you can be charged.

[3 marks]

_____

_____

_____

_____

_____

_____

(b) If you borrow £100 for a year, find the maximum amount of interest you can be charged. State any assumptions you have made.

[3 marks]

_____

_____

_____

_____

_____

_____

(c) An example of an advertised short-term loan is shown below.

Representative example	
Borrow	£100 for 13 days
Interest rate	292% pa (fixed)
One repayment	£110.40
Representative	1509% APR

Source: Wonga.com, 3 November 2016

Use your answers to parts **(a)** and **(b)** to comment on this advertisement. Is Wonga conforming to the FCA rule?

[4 marks]

_____

_____

_____

_____

_____

_____

_____

_____

_____

_____

_____

_____

_____

_____

(d) Theresa and Mark are discussing whether or not the APR figure is relevant for short-term loans. Give an argument in favour of each side of this debate.

[2 marks]

_____

_____

_____

_____

_____

_____

_____

_____

_____

7 Use **Speeding** on page 72.

Skid length (metres)	5	10	15	20	25	30	35	40	45	50	55	60
Speed (mph)	19	26	32	37	41	45	49	53	56	59	62	64

Length of marks and initial speed for a car skidding to rest

Police investigators have produced this data for the car and road conditions shown in the photograph on page 72. Write a brief report on whether the car had been driven at more than the speed limit of 40 mph.

You must show all necessary calculations and state any assumptions.

[8 marks]

_____

_____

_____

_____

_____

_____

_____

_____

_____

_____

_____

_____

_____

_____

_____

_____

_____

_____

_____

_____

_____

This is a practice paper so the wording on this cover page will not be *exactly* the same as on a real exam paper.

SET 1

Level 3 Certificate
MATHEMATICAL STUDIES

Set 1, Paper 2

Name: _____

Class: _____

Date: _____

Time allowed: 1 hour 30 minutes

Materials

For this paper you must have:

- a clean copy of the Preliminary material
- a scientific calculator or a graphics calculator
- a copy of the formulae sheet
- a ruler.

Instructions

- Use black ink or black ball-point pen. Draw diagrams in pencil.
- Fill in your name, class and the date at the top of this page.
- Answer all the questions.
- Do all rough work on this paper. Cross through any work that you do not want to be marked.
- In all calculations, show clearly how you work out your answer.
- The final answer to questions should be given to an appropriate degree of accuracy.
- You may not refer to the copy of the Preliminary material that was available prior to this examination. A clean copy is enclosed for your use.

Information

- The maximum mark for this paper is 60.
- The marks for each question are shown in brackets [ ].
- Use this as a guide as to how much time to spend on each question.

Advice

- Read each question carefully before you start to answer it.
- Keep an eye on the time.
- Try to answer every question.
- Check your answers if you have time at the end.

Preliminary material instructions

- The preliminary material will be given to you before your exam.
- You must not take annotated preliminary materials into the exam.
- You will be given a clean copy by your teacher.

Question			Mark
P2A	P2B	P2C	
1a	1a	1a	
1b	1b	1b	
1c	1c	1c	
2a	2a	2a	
2b	2b	2b	
2c	2c	2c	
3	3a	3a	
4	3b	3b	
5a	3c	4a	
5b	3d	4b	
6a	4a	5a	
6b	4b	5b	
6c	4b	5c	
6d	5a	5d	
7a	5b	5e	
7b	6a	6a	
	6b	6b	
		6c	
		6d	
Total			

81

European Referendum Information

Some information about the voting in the European Referendum is known with great accuracy. Examples of such factual data are given in Table 1.

Table 1

Total electorate	46 500 001
Remain	16 141 241
Leave	17 410 742
Rejected ballot	25 359

Other information about the voting is based upon estimates. For example, Table 2 shows the YouGov figures for how people of different ages voted. These figures are based upon an exit poll. Such polls are generally well-regarded because they are likely to reflect late swings in voting sentiment. However, this particular exit poll predicted a four-point lead for Remain.

Table 2

Age	Remain (%)	Leave (%)
18–24	75	25
25–49	56	44
50–64	44	56
65+	39	61

Source: YouGov exit poll

Figures for the turnouts of different age groups are even more problematical. For example, Table 3 has been widely circulated on social media but some critics of these figures have estimated turnouts as high as 65% for 18–24 year-olds and 90% for the over 65s.

Table 3

Age	Turnout (%)
18–24	36
25–34	58
35–44	72
45–54	75
55–64	81
65+	83

College survey

Josh has written this brief report on the views of the students and teachers at his college.

I asked each of the four teachers on the field trip how they had voted in the EU Referendum. It turned out that they had voted 3:1 in favour of Leave.

A diagram can be used to illustrate this finding.

Leave   Remain

I then similarly asked the students on the field trip how they would have voted, had they been registered. The students said they would have voted 2:1 in favour of Remain.

Leave   Remain

As you can see from the diagram, the staff and students of our college in general favoured Leave.

Set 1, Paper 2 Common

Answer the Paper 2 Common questions first, then move on to the questions for your optional paper: 2A (page 87), 2B (page 93) or 2C (page 98).

1 Use **European Referendum Information** in the Preliminary material.

(a) What reason for believing the accuracy of the YouGov poll (**Table 2**) is given in the article?

[1 mark]

_____

_____

(b) What reason for not believing the accuracy of the YouGov poll (**Table 2**) is given in the article?

[1 mark]

_____

_____

(c) The three statements given below were made during a debate.

Cheryl: *'The turnout was 72.2%.'*

Simon: *'51.9% of the electorate voted for Leave whereas 48.1% voted for Remain.'*

Sharon: *'If the 1.6 million 16–17 year olds had been allowed to vote, they would have voted Remain and reversed the result of the referendum.'*

Critically analyse these statements. In each case, justify your conclusions with numerical calculations.

For Sharon's statement, state any assumptions you have made.

[11 marks]

Cheryl's statement:

_____

_____

_____

_____

_____

_____

_____

_____

_____

Simon's statement:

_____

_____

_____

_____

_____

_____

_____

_____

_____

Sharon's statement:

_____

_____

_____

_____

_____

_____

_____

_____

_____

_____

_____

_____

2 Use **College survey** in the Preliminary material.

(a) What type of sampling method was used in this survey?

[1 mark]

_____

_____

_____

_____

_____

_____

(b) State two reasons why this was not a good method for sampling the teaching staff.

[2 marks]

_____

_____

_____

_____

_____

_____

(c) Critically analyse both the diagram that Josh used to display his results and his conclusion from this diagram that 'the staff and students of our college in general favoured Leave.'

[4 marks]

_____

_____

_____

_____

_____

_____

_____

_____

_____

_____

_____

Common questions can be found at the beginning of Paper 2 on page 84.

3 The reaction times (in milliseconds) for a group of ten female tennis professionals were:

198 222 203 225 233 220 206 201 182 199

In the same test, the average reaction time for women of similar ages and BMIs as the tennis players was 215 milliseconds.

The reaction times of the tennis players may be assumed to follow a normal distribution with mean μ and variance 225. Calculate a 90% symmetric confidence interval for μ and then comment on whether the tennis players have faster reactions than average.

[7 marks]

4 The goals scored for and against, and the points achieved by ten premier league football teams in the 2015/2016 season were:

Team	For	Against	Points
Leicester City	68	36	81
Tottenham Hotspur	69	35	70
Manchester United	49	35	66
West Ham United	65	51	62
Stoke City	41	55	51
Everton	59	55	47
Watford Town	40	50	45
Crystal Palace	39	51	42
Sunderland	48	62	39
Norwich City	39	67	34

Source: 2015/2016 EPL

Use statistical analyses and reasoning to comment on whether a good attack or a good defence is the most effective for achieving a high number of points.

[6 marks]

_____

_____

_____

_____

_____

_____

_____

_____

_____

_____

_____

_____

_____

_____

_____

_____

_____

_____

5 The daily sales in a store are normally distributed with mean £10 000 and standard deviation £1000.

(a) What is the probability that a particular day's sales are less than £9000?

[2 marks]

_____

_____

_____

_____

_____

_____

_____

_____

_____

_____

(b) Staff receive bonuses for each day that they work when sales exceed £12 000. One member of staff works 250 days in a year. For how many days can they expect a bonus?

[4 marks]

_____

_____

_____

_____

_____

_____

_____

_____

_____

_____

_____

_____

6 Lichens are especially sensitive to air pollution and are widely used as bio-indicators. The scatter diagram illustrates the relationship between nitrogen deposition (measured in kg per hectare per year) and the proportion of nitrogen-tolerant lichen on trees at 12 sites in North America.

(a) For these 12 sites, state the mean values of

Nitrogen deposition ....

Nitrogen-tolerant lichen ....%

[2 marks]

(b) Find the equation of the regression line of P on N. Draw the regression line on the scatter diagram. You may use this table if you wish.

[6 marks]

N											
P											

(c) In another site in North America, the nitrogen deposition is 4.0 kg per hectare per year. What would you expect the proportion of nitrogen-tolerant lichen to be?

[2 marks]

(d) Give two reasons why the regression line analysis in parts (a), (b) and (c) is not useful for a site in the UK where the nitrogen deposition is 2.0 kg per hectare per year.

[2 marks]

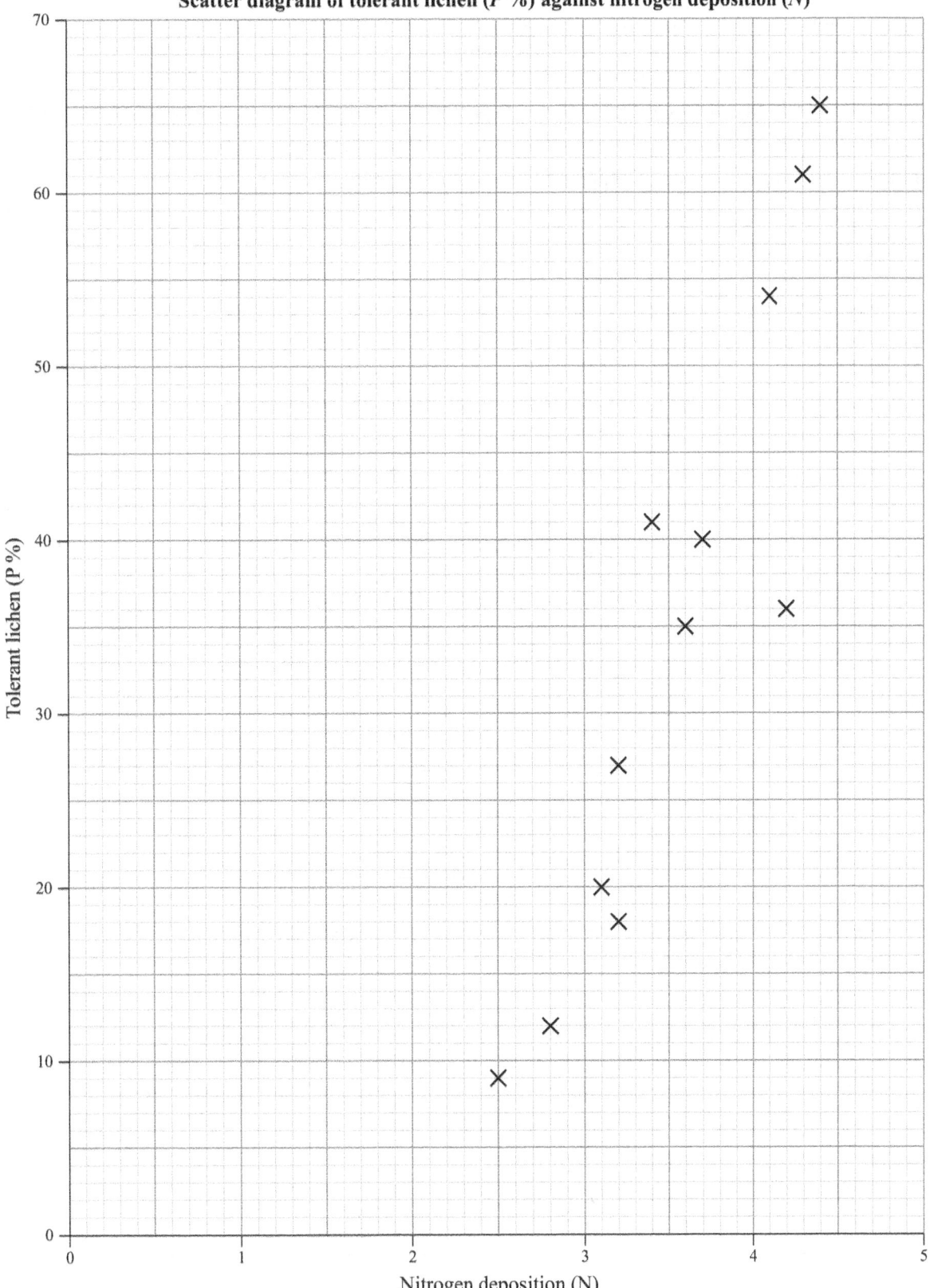

Scatter diagram of tolerant lichen (*P* %) against nitrogen deposition (*N*)

7 The typical sugar content of a 250 ml cola drink is 26.5 g. The claims of two rival producers of 250 ml apple juice drinks are shown below.

June's Juice: '*On average our apple juice drinks have less sugar than Ollie's Orchard's drinks.*'

Ollie's Orchard: '*Our drinks are more likely than June's Juice's drinks to have less sugar than a typical cola drink.*'

(a) Explain how it is possible for both of these claims to be true.

[2 marks]

_____

_____

_____

(b) The sugar content of June's Juice's drinks have mean 24 g and s.d. 2 g.

The sugar content of Ollie's Orchard's drinks have mean 25 g and s.d. 1 g.

One bottle of each drink is chosen at random. What is the probability that both will have less sugar than a typical cola drink? You must show your working, using a suitable probability distribution. State one assumption you have made.

[7 marks]

_____

_____

_____

_____

_____

_____

_____

_____

_____

_____

_____

_____

_____

_____

_____

Set 1, Paper 2B

Common questions can be found at the beginning of Paper 2 on page 84.

3 A contestant in a TV gameshow can choose one of four indistinguishable boxes and will then win the contents of that box.

| 1p | £10 | £5000 | £1 million |

(a) What are the contestant's expected winnings?

[3 marks]

_____

_____

_____

(b) Why might the contestant accept an amount £A to **not** choose any box even if £A is less than the answer to part (a)?

[2 marks]

_____

_____

_____

(c) The TV company paid a large insurance premium to underwrite the £1 million prize. So, if the contestant chooses the box with this prize, it is paid by the insurance company and not by the TV company. If the contestant chooses a box, find the expected cost to:

(i) the TV company

(ii) the insurance company.

[3 marks]

_____

_____

_____

_____

(d) Explain the connection between the answers to parts (a) and (c).

[2 marks]

_____

_____

_____

4 The data-handling system in a company is to be upgraded. The work involved has been divided into a number of activities as shown in the table.

Activity	Immediate predecessor	Duration (weeks)
A Plan system	–	1
B Approval	A	1
C Select hardware platform	B	1
D Install hardware	C	3
E Programming analysis	B	2
F Program support modules	E	2
G Program core modules	E	3
H Quality assurance	D, F, G	2
I Initial training	G	1
J Final training	H, I	1

(a) Construct an activity network, showing early and late times.

[7 marks]

(b) List the critical path. If the work needs to be speeded up, suggest, with a reason, how this might be achieved.

[3 marks]

_____

_____

_____

_____

_____

_____

_____

_____

(c) Construct a Gantt chart for this project.

[4 marks]

5 Suppose you have a legal claim for compensation. It is likely that you will engage a lawyer on a no-win, no-fee basis.

If you win the case, your lawyer will take a percentage of your compensation called a *success fee deduction*.

If you lose, you pay no fees to your lawyer but can be liable for the defendant's costs.

You are expecting compensation of £20K if you win but are expecting to pay costs of £10K if you lose. On a comparison website, you input the details of your claim and have to decide between these two firms.

Dodson & Fogg	Win 90% of such cases	Success fee deduction 20%
Jarndyce & Jarndyce	Win 80% of such cases	Success fee deduction 10%

(a) Which firm should you choose? Justify your choice with numerical calculations.

[8 marks]

_____

_____

_____

_____

_____

_____

_____

_____

_____

_____

_____

_____

_____

_____

_____

_____

_____

_____

_____

_____

_____

(b) In practice, claimants are recommended to take out insurance against losing their claim for compensation. In return for a premium, the insurance company will then pay any costs the claimant is liable for if they lose the case.

What premium is an insurance company likely to charge for a case that has a 10% chance of failing and for which they would then incur costs of £10K?

[2 marks]

_____

_____

_____

_____

_____

6 The numbers on the Venn diagram represent percentages of voters in a referendum.

KEY

F   Voted for the proposal
O   Aged over 40
D   Educated to degree level

(a) Find the probability that someone with a degree voted in favour of the proposal.

[3 marks]

_____

_____

_____

_____

_____

(b) What percentage of those who voted against the proposal are under 40 with a degree?

[3 marks]

_____

_____

_____

_____

_____

Common questions can be found at the beginning of Paper 2 on page 84.

3 Two velocity–time graphs are as shown.

(a) v

(b) v

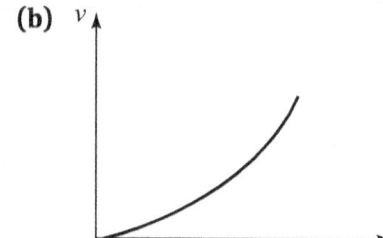

In each case, describe the motion and suggest a possible equation for v in terms of t.

(a)

[3 marks]

_____

_____

_____

_____

_____

_____

_____

_____

(b)

[3 marks]

_____

_____

_____

_____

_____

_____

_____

_____

4 The graph shows the proportion of a basic rate taxpayer's salary that is paid in tax. The curve from $(11, 0)$ to $(43, 14.9)$ can be modelled by the quadratic equation

$$y = (x-11)\left(1-\frac{x}{c}\right)$$ for a suitable constant c

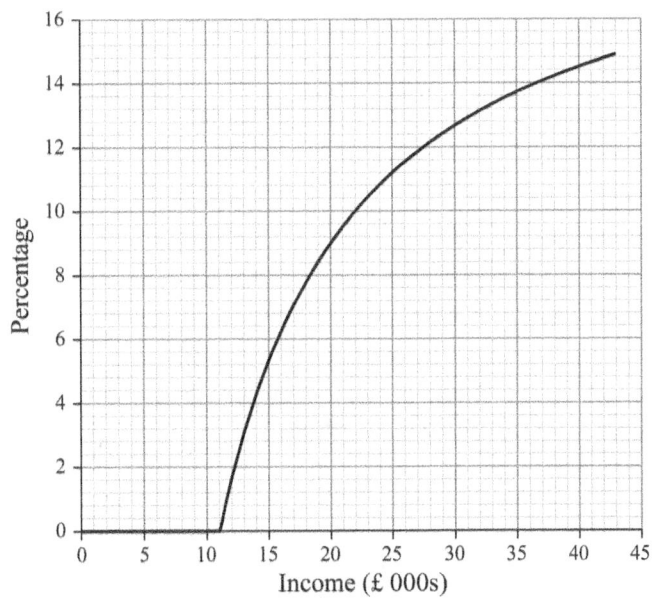

(a) Find the value of c which will ensure that the quadratic curve passes through $(40, 14.5)$.

[4 marks]

_____

_____

_____

_____

_____

_____

_____

(b) For your value of c, sketch the quadratic curve on the graph in part **(a)**. Show any necessary calculations.

[3 marks]

_____

_____

_____

_____

_____

5 The graph shows how radioactive decay causes the numbers of uranium and lead atoms in a rock sample to change over time.

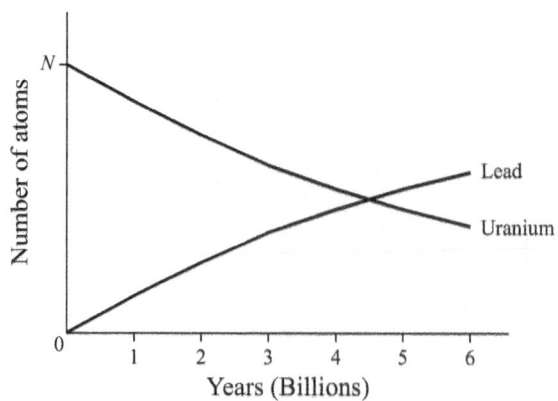

(a) How many years does it take for the number of uranium atoms to reduce to 75% of its initial value? Draw lines on the graph to illustrate your method.

[3 marks]

_____

_____

_____

_____

_____

_____

_____

_____

(b) When formed, the mineral Zircon contains no lead atoms. In Australia, many samples of Zircon contain roughly equal numbers of lead and uranium atoms. What does this imply about the age of the Earth? State any assumptions you have made.

[4 marks]

_____

_____

_____

_____

_____

_____

_____

A formula for the number of uranium atoms in a sample of Zircon is given by

$$Ne^{-kt}$$

where N is the initial number and t is the time in billions of years.

(c) Explain why

$$e^{-4.5k} = \frac{1}{2}$$

[3 marks]

_____

_____

_____

_____

_____

_____

_____

(d) Hence find k.

[3 marks]

_____

_____

_____

_____

_____

_____

_____

(e) State a formula for the number of lead atoms in the Zircon sample.

[2 marks]

_____

_____

_____

_____

_____

_____

6 In a chemical reaction, the strength of a solution increases as shown on the graph.

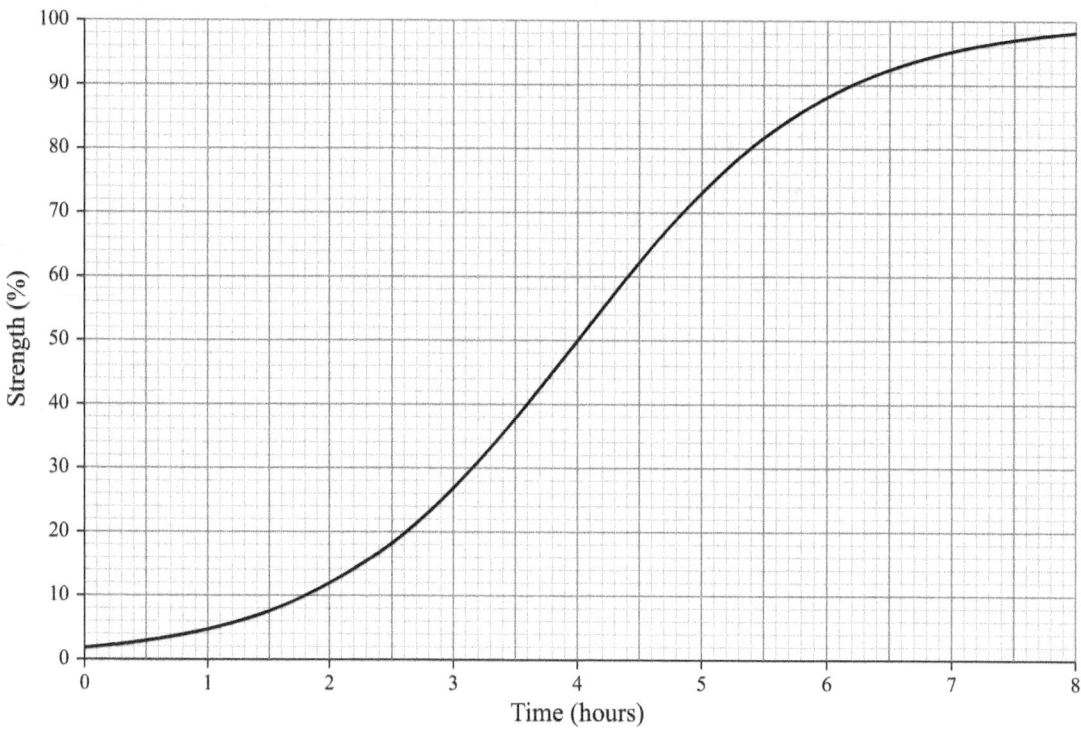

(a) How long does it take for the strength to reach 80%?

[2 marks]

_____

_____

_____

(b) By drawing a tangent to the curve, find the gradient of the curve at $t = 3$.

[3 marks]

_____

_____

_____

_____

(c) Explain the meaning of this gradient in context.

[2 marks]

_____

_____

_____

_____

(d) Sketch a graph of rate of change of strength against strength and find the coordinates of the maximum point of this new graph.

[5 marks]

SET 2

Level 3 Certificate MATHEMATICAL STUDIES

Set 2, Paper 1

Name: _____

Class: _____

Date: _____   **Time allowed:** 1 hour 30 minutes

Materials

For this paper you must have:

- a clean copy of the Preliminary material
- a scientific calculator or a graphics calculator
- a copy of the formulae sheet
- a ruler.

Instructions

- Use black ink or black ball-point pen. Draw diagrams in pencil.
- Fill in your name, class and the date at the top of this page.
- Answer all the questions.
- Do all rough work on this paper. Cross through any work that you do not want to be marked.
- In all calculations, show clearly how you work out your answer.
- The final answer to questions should be given to an appropriate degree of accuracy.
- You may not refer to the copy of the Preliminary material that was available prior to this examination. A clean copy is enclosed for your use.

Information

- The maximum mark for this paper is 60.
- The marks for each question are shown in brackets [ ].
- Use this as a guide as to how much time to spend on each question.

Advice

- Read each question carefully before you start to answer it.
- Keep an eye on the time.
- Try to answer every question.
- Check your answers if you have time at the end.

Preliminary material instructions

- The preliminary material will be given to you before your exam.
- You must not take annotated preliminary materials into the exam.
- You will be given a clean copy by your teacher.

Question	Mark
1a	
1b	
1c	
1d	
2a	
2bi	
2bii	
3	
4	
5ai	
5aii	
5aiii	
5b	
6a	
6bi	
6bii	
7a	
7b	
Total	

Set 2
Practice Paper 1

Childcare

In 2016, all 3- and 4-year-old children could get 570 hours of free childcare per year, usually taken as 15 hours per week for 38 weeks. The take-up rate was 95%.

The government carried out a consultation about increasing the offer of free childcare to working parents from 15 to 30 hours per week. The consultation included online questionnaires as well as direct engagement with key stakeholders such as local authorities and childcare providers.

Nursery regulations

These are some of the regulations that apply to nursery staff:

- The manager must have a level 3 qualification and at least 2 years' experience.
- At least half of the remaining staff must have a level 2 qualification.

Staff:child ratios

Age of children (years)	Minimum staff:child ratio
Under 2	1:3
2	1:4
3 and over	1:8

Source: Statutory framework for the early years foundation stage, www.gov.uk

Salary guides

The salaries paid to people who work in nurseries depend on the size of the nursery and its location, as well as the workers' qualifications and experience.

Job title	Salary (per annum)	Hours (per week)
Nursery manager	£22 000–£35 000	35–40
Nursery worker	£14 000–£25 000	35–40

Source: https://nationalcareersservice.direct.gov.uk

1 A car magazine wants to find out how much, on average, learner drivers spend on driving lessons and how far they drive before passing their tests.

(a) What type of data is the amount spent by learner drivers on driving lessons?

Tick all the boxes that apply.

qualitative   discrete   continuous   quantitative

☐   ☐   ☐   ☐

[2 marks]

(b) The magazine requests data from the two nearest driving schools.
What method of sampling is this?

[1 mark]

_____

(c) Describe in detail how the magazine could use quota sampling.

[3 marks]

_____

_____

_____

_____

_____

(d) A driving instructor puts this advertisement in the magazine.

Pass in a week! £761

Includes cost of driving test + 30 hours in car
(2 hours of this time is for attending the test)

Estimate the distance a learner on this course will drive before taking the test.
State any assumptions you have made.

[4 marks]

_____

_____

_____

_____

_____

_____

2 (a) Related to interest rates, what do the following abbreviations stand for?

(i) APR _____

(ii) AER _____

[2 marks]

(b) Jack invests £800 in a savings account.

The compound interest rate is fixed at 5% each year.

Jack does not subsequently add any money or withdraw any money from this account.

(i) How many years will it take for the amount in the account to double?

[3 marks]

_____

_____

_____

_____

_____

_____

_____

_____

_____

_____

_____

_____

_____

(ii) Explain why the investment at that time is not likely to buy twice as much as it did when Jack invested his money.

[1 mark]

_____

_____

_____

_____

_____

_____

3 The table gives the reaction times of adults who took part in an experiment to test their reaction times to a visual stimulus.

Reaction time (t milliseconds)	Number of adults
$160 \leq t < 200$	4
$200 \leq t < 220$	14
$220 \leq t < 240$	16
$240 \leq t < 260$	23
$260 \leq t < 280$	15
$280 \leq t < 320$	6
$320 \leq t < 400$	2

The same adults took part in an experiment to test their reaction times to an auditory stimulus. The results are illustrated by this histogram.

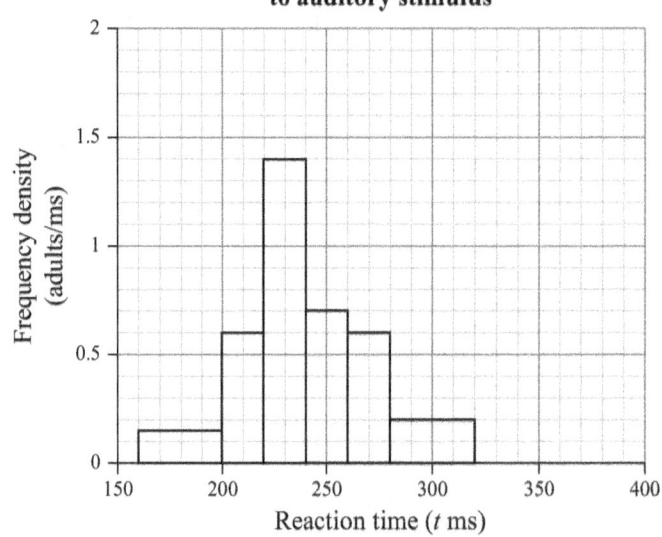

Histogram showing reaction times to auditory stimulus

Frequency density (adults/ms) vs Reaction time (t ms)

Compare the distributions of reaction times.

Use the grid on the following page if you wish.

[7 marks]

_____

_____

_____

_____

_____

_____

_____

4 Use **Income Tax and National Insurance 2016–2017** on page 70.

During the year 2016–2017, Sayed had an annual salary of £34 000.

His personal tax allowance was £11 000.

Sayed says that his monthly rent of £460 was more than 20% of his take-home pay.

Is Sayed correct? You must show your working.

[7 marks]

5 Astrid has a mortgage for £140 000. The gross annual interest rate is 4%.

Astrid makes monthly repayments of £1600.

(a) Astrid uses the recurrence relation

$$A_{n+1} = 1.04A_n - 19\,200$$

to calculate the total amount £A_{n+1} she owes at the end of the $n+1$ th year.

(i) Explain the terms $1.04A_n$ and $19\,200$ in the recurrence relation.

[2 marks]

_____

_____

_____

_____

(ii) Use the recurrence relation to complete the table to give the amount of the mortgage debt outstanding at the end of each of the first five years.

Give your values correct to the nearest penny.

n	A_n (£)
0	140 000.00
1	
2	
3	
4	
5	

[3 marks]

(iii) Using your answer to part (a) (ii), find the amount Astrid will have paid off her mortgage in the first five years.

_____

[2 marks]

(b) If Astrid halved her repayments, explain why the time it would take her to repay the mortgage is more than twice what it was.

[2 marks]

_____

_____

_____

_____

_____

6 A company is comparing the hours worked and earnings of its full-time employees with national statistics.

(a) The table gives the mean number of hours overtime worked by the company's male and female employees per week.

	Number of employees	Mean overtime hours per week
Male	116	1.4
Female	64	0.5

Calculate the mean number of overtime hours per employee per week.

[3 marks]

_____

_____

_____

_____

(b) The table shows the distribution of gross weekly earnings of the company's employees.

Gross full-time earnings (£x per week)	Number of employees
$200 < x \leq 300$	12
$300 < x \leq 400$	26
$400 < x \leq 500$	48
$500 < x \leq 600$	72
$600 < x \leq 800$	18
$800 < x \leq 1000$	4

National statistics gave the following results:

	Lower Quartile	Median	Upper Quartile
Full-time gross weekly earnings	£389.20	£538.70	£762.40

(i) Explain why the median is usually used, rather than the mean, in national earnings statistics.

[1 mark]

_____

_____

_____

_____

(ii) The company says that, on average, their employees earn more than the national average and that their earnings are less varied.

Use the given data to comment on the company's statement.

You may use the grid below if you wish.

[7 marks]

_____

_____

_____

_____

_____

_____

_____

_____

_____

_____

_____

_____

7   Use **Childcare** on page 105.

   (a) Give one advantage and one disadvantage of using an online consultation.

   Advantage: _____

   _____

   Disadvantage: _____

   _____

                                                                          [2 marks]

   (b) A local authority has a population of 96 thousand.
       Estimate how much it costs this local authority each year to provide 570 hours of childcare
       for the 3 and 4 year olds in its population.

       State any assumptions you have made. You must show your working.

                                                                          [8 marks]

This is a practice paper so the wording on this cover page will not be *exactly* the same as on a real exam paper.

SET 2

Level 3 Certificate
MATHEMATICAL STUDIES

Set 2, Paper 2

Name: _____

Class: _____

Date: _____

Time allowed: 1 hour 30 minutes

Materials

For this paper you must have:

- a clean copy of the Preliminary material
- a scientific calculator or a graphics calculator
- a copy of the formulae sheet
- a ruler.

Instructions

- Use black ink or black ball-point pen. Draw diagrams in pencil.
- Fill in your name, class and the date at the top of this page.
- Answer all the questions.
- Do all rough work on this paper. Cross through any work that you do not want to be marked.
- In all calculations, show clearly how you work out your answer.
- The final answer to questions should be given to an appropriate degree of accuracy.
- You may not refer to the copy of the Preliminary material that was available prior to this examination. A clean copy is enclosed for your use.

Information

- The maximum mark for this paper is 60.
- The marks for each question are shown in brackets [ ].
- Use this as a guide as to how much time to spend on each question.

Advice

- Read each question carefully before you start to answer it.
- Keep an eye on the time.
- Try to answer every question.
- Check your answers if you have time at the end.

Preliminary material instructions

- The preliminary material will be given to you before your exam.
- You must not take annotated preliminary materials into the exam.
- You will be given a clean copy by your teacher.

Question			Mark
P2A	P2B	P2C	
1a	1a	1a	
1b	1b	1b	
2a	2a	2a	
2b	2b	2b	
2c	2c	2c	
2d	2d	2d	
2e	2e	2e	
3	3a	3a	
4a	3b	3b	
4b	4a	3c	
4c	4b	4a	
5a	4c	4b	
5b	4d	4c	
5c	5	4d	
6a	6a	5a	
6b	6b	5b	
7	6c	5c	
	6d	6a	
	7a	6b	
	7b	7a	
		7b	
Total			

115

Lambing

A student records the weights, in kilograms, of the 24 lambs born on the family farm in Spring 2016.

```
2 | 0
1 | 9
1 | 8
1 | 7 7 7 7
1 | 6 6 6
1 | 5 5 5 5
1 | 4 4 4 4 4 4
1 | 3 3 3
1 |
1 | 1
```

Key

1 | 7 represents 1.7 kg

She also represents these data on a box and whisker diagram.

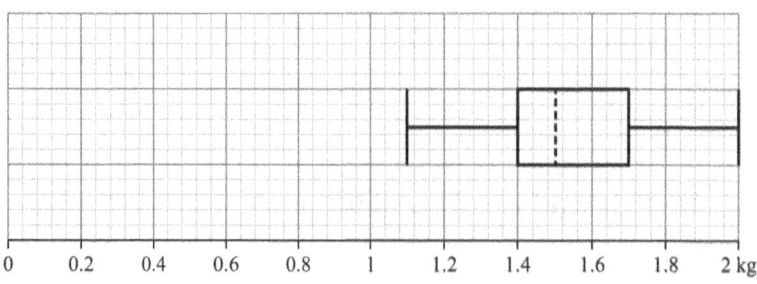

Petrol prices

...as crude rallies...

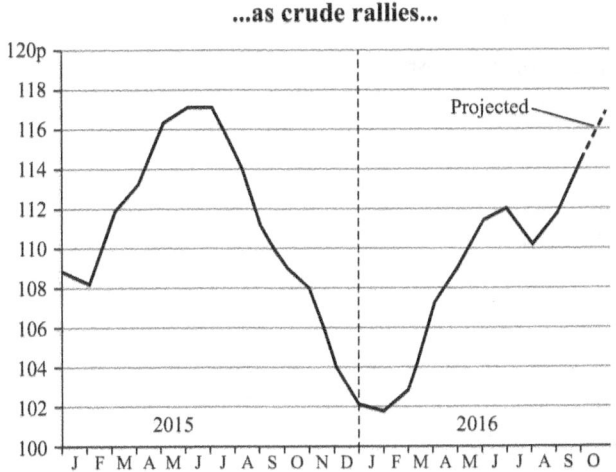

...as crude rallies...

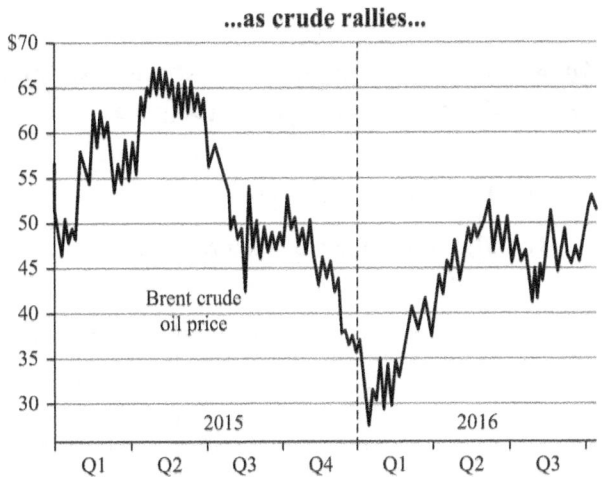

What you're paying at the pump

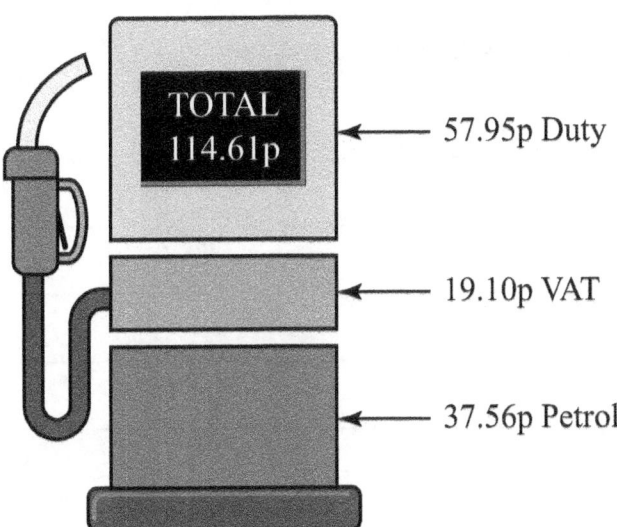

TOTAL 114.61p

57.95p Duty

19.10p VAT

37.56p Petrol

Source: The Times, 15 October 2016

Set 2, Paper 2 Common

Answer the Paper 2 Common questions first, then move on to the questions for your optional paper: 2A (page 121), 2B (page 129) or 2C (page 135).

1   Use **Lambing** on page 116.

   (a) The student decides to draw a histogram to illustrate the data.

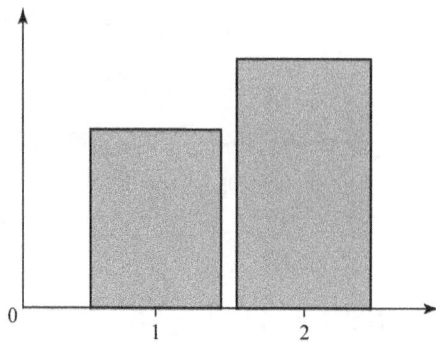

   Critically analyse the student's diagram.

   [4 marks]

   _____

   _____

   _____

   _____

   _____

   _____

   _____

   (b) The student's mother is surprised that the range of weights shown on the box and whisker diagram is 0.9 kg. She says: 'I remember that one lamb was almost exactly 1 kg heavier than another'. How can both the student and her mother be correct?

   [2 marks]

   _____

   _____

   _____

   _____

   _____

   _____

2 Use **Petrol prices** on page 117.

(a) Following the publication of the graphs, two statements about petrol prices were:

A: *'Drivers are being fleeced. Prices at the pump go up when oil prices rise but stay up when oil prices drop.'*

B: *'Prices at the pump mirror oil prices but smooth out some of the fluctuations.'*

Does the data support either of these two statements?

[3 marks]

_____

_____

_____

_____

_____

_____

_____

_____

_____

(b) What three features of the graphs of pump prices and crude oil prices make them difficult to compare?

[3 marks]

_____

_____

_____

_____

_____

_____

_____

_____

_____

_____

(c) *'Even if oil were free, drivers would pay 69.54 pence per litre.'*

Justify this assertion.

[3 marks]

_____

_____

_____

_____

_____

_____

(d) A model for the price of petrol (P pence per litre) is

$$P = 0.5B + 85$$

where $\$B$ is the cost of crude oil. Comment on the accuracy of this model by considering prices on two different occasions.

[3 marks]

_____

_____

_____

_____

_____

_____

(e) Oil industry insiders have a simple rule:

'A $2 change in the price of oil results in ....'

Use the formula of part **(d)** to complete the statement of this rule.

[2 marks]

_____

_____

_____

_____

_____

_____

_____

Set 2, Paper 2A

Common questions can be found at the beginning of Paper 2 on page 118.

3 A company claims that its bags of gravel contain on average 25 kilograms.

Assume that the weight, X kg, of gravel in a bag can be modelled by a normal variable with unknown mean μ kg and known standard deviation 0.3 kg.

A random sample of 10 bags from the company contained the following weights in kilograms:

   25.1   24.5   25.0   24.4   25.3   25.1   24.5   25.2   24.3   25.1

Calculate a 98% confidence interval for μ and comment on the claim that bags contain, on average, 25 kg of gravel.

[6 marks]

4 For eight suburbs of a town, the scatter graph shows the population density, *P* people per hectare, plotted against distance, *d* kilometres, from the centre of the town.

The graph also shows the line of best fit.

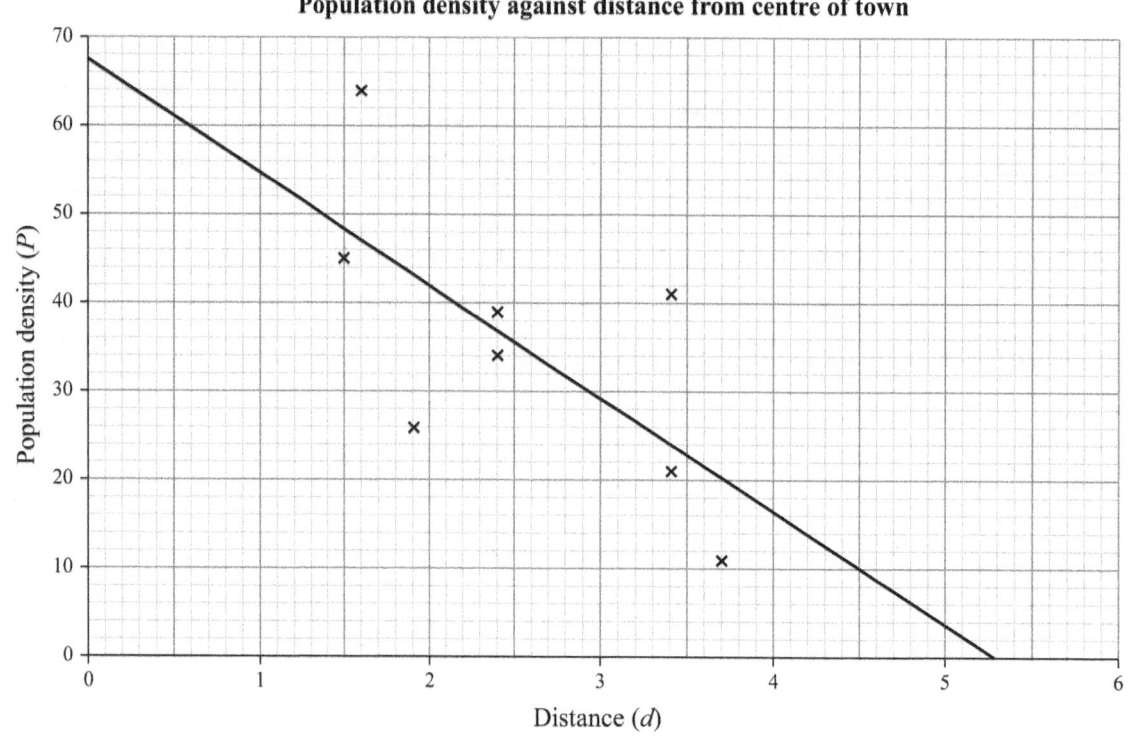

Population density against distance from centre of town

(a) Find and interpret the gradient of the line of best fit.

[3 marks]

(b) Find the product-moment correlation coefficient and interpret your result in context.
You may use the table below if you wish.

[3 marks]

_____

_____

_____

_____

_____

_____

_____

_____

_____

_____

_____

d								
P								

(c) A student uses the line of best fit to estimate the population densities of suburbs at distances of 0.5 km, 3 km and 6 km from the centre.

Comment on the appropriateness or otherwise of this procedure.

[2 marks]

_____

_____

_____

_____

_____

_____

_____

_____

_____

5 The table shows the Gross Domestic Product (GDP) of the G7 countries in trillions of US$. Also shown are the numbers of gold medals won at the 2016 Olympics in Rio de Janeiro.

Country	GDP (US$trillions)	Gold medals
Canada	1.7	4
France	2.8	10
Germany	3.6	17
Italy	2.2	8
Japan	5.9	12
UK	2.4	27
USA	15.1	46

(a) Plot a scatter graph of number of gold medals against GDP.

[2 marks]

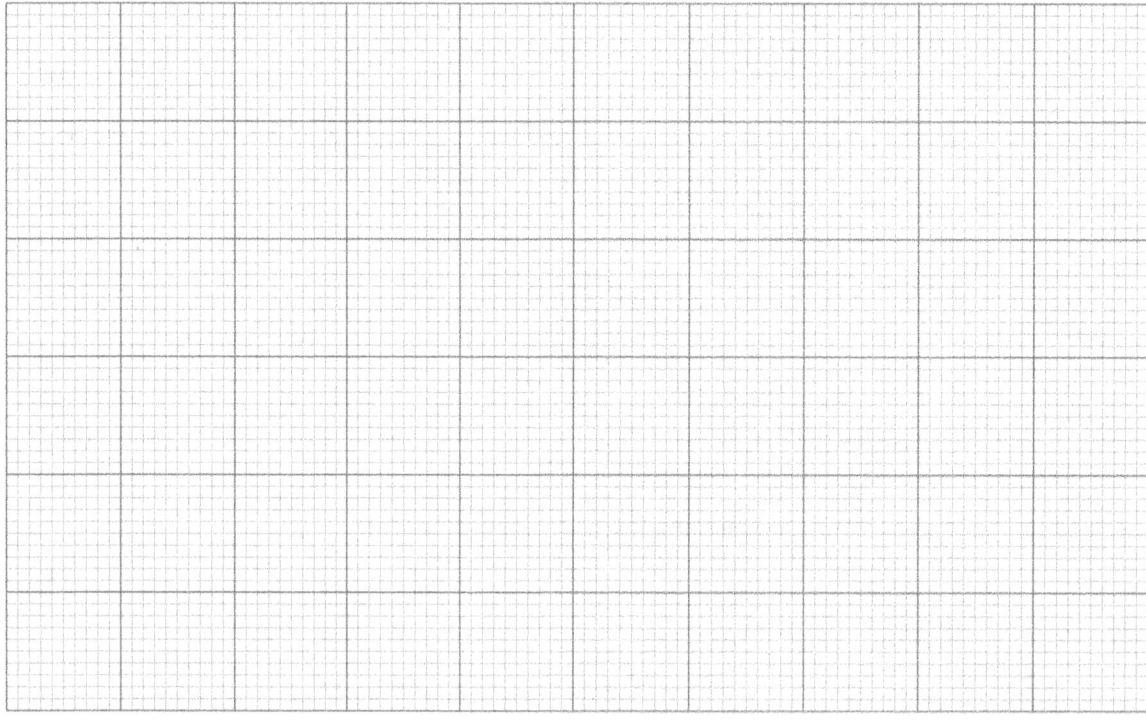

(b) Calculate the equation of the regression line for gold medals against GDP and draw this line on your graph.

[4 marks]

_____

_____

_____

_____

_____

_____

_____

_____

_____

_____

_____

_____

_____

_____

_____

_____

_____

(c) Explain the significance of a point representing a country being above or below the regression line.

[1 mark]

_____

_____

_____

_____

_____

_____

_____

6 The shoe size chart shows the adult shoe sizes used in the UK and EU, and the foot lengths that a shoe manufacturer designs them to fit.

UK	EU	Foot length (cm)
2	35	21.2
3	36	22.1
4	37	22.9
5	38	23.7
6	39	24.6
7	41	25.4
8	42	26.3
9	43	27.2
10	45	28.0
11	46	28.9
12	47	29.8
13	48	30.6
14	49	31.4
15	51	32.3

(a) Compare the correlation between UK shoe sizes and foot length with that between EU shoe sizes and foot length. You may use the grids below if you wish.

[3 marks]

_____

_____

_____

_____

_____

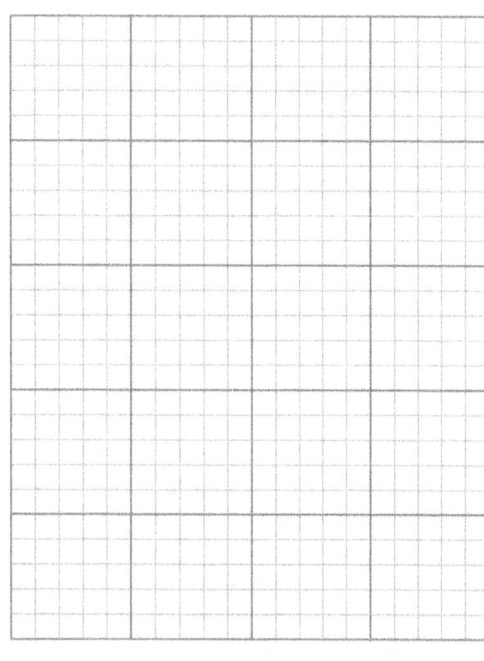 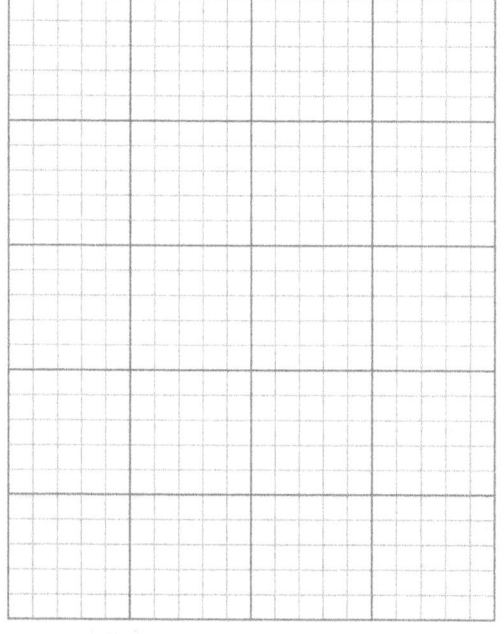

(b) In the UK, the mean length of women's feet is 241.1 mm with standard deviation 12.7 mm.

The shoe manufacturer wants to make shoes that will fit women whose foot lengths lie between the 5th and the 95th percentiles of this distribution.

Advise the company which UK sizes it should make.

State any assumptions you have made.

[7 marks]

_____

_____

_____

_____

_____

_____

_____

_____

_____

_____

_____

_____

_____

_____

_____

_____

_____

_____

_____

_____

_____

_____

7   Sam's hens lay eggs with a mean weight of 60 grams and standard deviation 5 grams.
    The table shows the weight categories for eggs.

    Sam keeps any very large and small eggs for his own use.
    He sells the large and medium eggs in dozens at the prices given in the table.

Size	Weight (x grams)	Price (per dozen)
Very large	$x \geq 73$	–
Large	$63 \leq x < 73$	£1
Medium	$53 \leq x < 63$	80 pence
Small	$x < 53$	–

    Calculate the income that Sam can expect to earn from 3000 eggs laid by his hens.
    State any assumptions you have made.

    [9 marks]

Set 2, Paper 2B

Common questions can be found at the beginning of Paper 2 on page 118.

3 (a) A car has come to the end of its 3-year manufacturer's warranty. For years 4 to 7 of the car's life, the annual cost of repairs are modelled in the table:

Cost of repair	£0	£220	£1000
Likelihood	0.85	0.1	0.05

What is the expected cost of repairs over this period?

[3 marks]

_____

_____

_____

_____

(b) The car in part (a) has the same expected cost of repairs as a BMW 1 Series 118d SE. The annual cost of insuring against breakdown costs for such a car are shown for six leading insurers:

Insurer	ALA	Click 4	Go Car	Used Vehicle Warranty	Warranty Direct	Warranty wise
Annual cost	£367	£396	£354	£180	£452	£585

Source: Which? Car Survey

Based on these figures, write a brief report for the owner of the car in part (a), setting out the advantages and disadvantages of insuring against breakdown costs.

[4 marks]

_____

_____

_____

_____

_____

_____

_____

_____

4 The Venn diagram shows the percentages of people in work who are female (F) and part time (T).

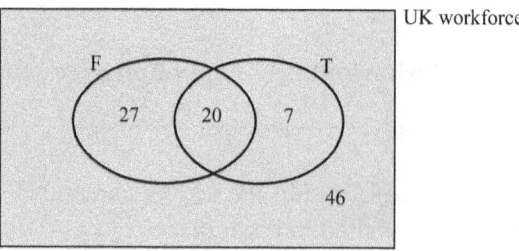

UK workforce

F   27   20   7   T

46

(a) Who are represented by the 46% region?

[1 mark]

_____

_____

_____

(b) What is the probability that a randomly-chosen worker is a woman working part time?

[2 marks]

_____

_____

_____

(c) An election candidate makes the following statement:

'Of the workforce, about half are men and about a quarter are part time. So, roughly an eighth of the workforce are men working part time.'

What calculation has the candidate carried out? Comment on whether the candidate is correct and explain your answer.

[3 marks]

_____

_____

_____

_____

_____

_____

_____

_____

_____

(d) An alternative way of representing the data is to use a tree diagram. Complete the probabilities on this tree diagram.

[5 marks]

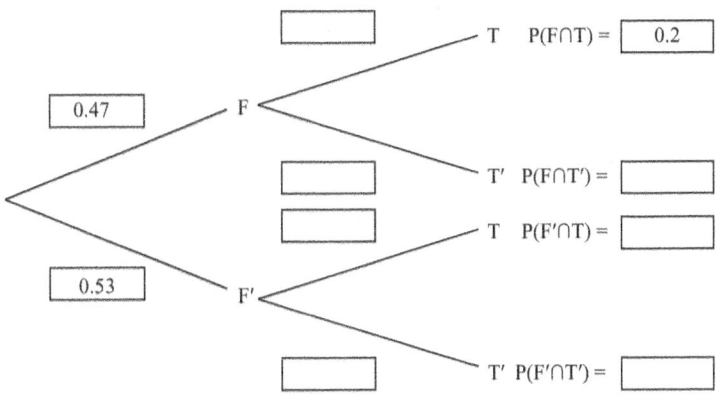

F   P(F∩T) = 0.2

T'   P(F∩T') =

T   P(F'∩T) =

T'   P(F'∩T') =

5 It is stated that 'the average annual salary of a female full-time worker is £25K'.

Name two possible meanings for the word 'average' in this statement and make three statements about the advantages/disadvantages of either or both of the meanings.

[4 marks]

_____

_____

_____

_____

_____

_____

_____

_____

_____

_____

_____

_____

_____

_____

_____

_____

_____

6   Steve is planning to decorate a room in his flat. He decides on the order of the tasks and estimates how long they will take him to complete.

Activity	Immediate predecessor	Duration (hours)
A Clear room and protect carpet	–	2
B Strip wallpaper	A	4
C Rub down woodwork	A	2
D Paint ceiling	B	2
E Undercoat and gloss woodwork	B,C	8
F Wait for gloss to dry	E	8
G Wallpaper	D,F	12
H Restore room	G	2

(a) Complete this activity network, showing early and late times.

[3 marks]

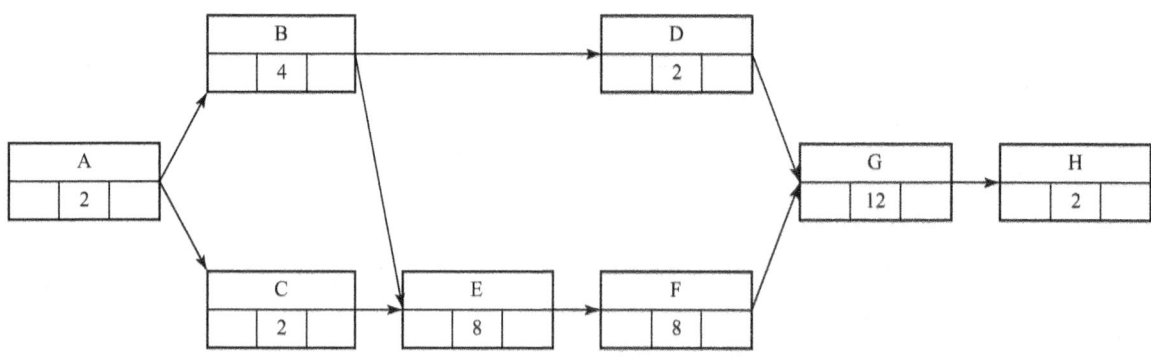

(b) List the critical path and state its length.

[2 marks]

_____

_____

_____

(c) Draw a Gantt chart for this project.

[3 marks]

(d) How long would it take for Steve to do the work on his own? Explain your answer. State any assumptions you have made.

[3 marks]

_____

_____

_____

_____

_____

_____

_____

_____

_____

7   A contractor will incur a £P penalty if a project is delayed. If she wishes, she can choose to undertake just one of the two control measures shown in the table.

Measure	Cost of measure	Probability of delay if measure is taken
A	£500	0.1
B	£1000	0.05

(a) Of these two measures, explain why she should prefer to take measure A if the penalty is less than £10 000 but, otherwise, she should prefer measure B.

[3 marks]

_____

_____

_____

_____

_____

_____

_____

(b) The probability of delay is 0.2 if she takes no control measure. Advise her on what to do.

[4 marks]

_____

_____

_____

_____

_____

_____

_____

_____

_____

_____

Set 2, Paper 2C

Common questions can be found at the beginning of Paper 2 on page 118.

3 On a comparison website, two interest-only mortgages, fixed for two years, are:

Ingotts
Competitive interest rate 1.79% fixed for 2 years. Low arrangement fee £485
Representative example   Borrow £100 000
Total cost for 2 years £485 + 1790 + 1790 = £4065

Borsetshire Building Society
No magic, no gimmicks. Just a down-to-Earth interest rate.
Fixed rate at 1.37% for 2 years. Booking fee (£150); Valuation fee (£336); Funds transfer fee (£25); Mortgage discharge fee (£75); Deeds release fee (£50); Legal fee (£250); Application fee (£995). Eligible for first-time buyers, home movers.

(a) Show that borrowing £100 000 from Borsetshire Building Society has a total cost of £4621.

[2 marks]

_____

_____

_____

_____

_____

_____

(b) A formula for the cost, $£C$ of borrowing $£A$ from Ingotts is

$$C = 485 + 0.0358A$$

Find the equivalent formula for Borsetshire Building Society.

[2 marks]

_____

_____

_____

_____

_____

(c) Advise a prospective borrower which of these two mortgages to choose according to the size of their intended mortgage. State any assumptions you have made.

You can use the graph paper below.

[6 marks]

_____

_____

_____

_____

_____

_____

_____

_____

_____

_____

_____

_____

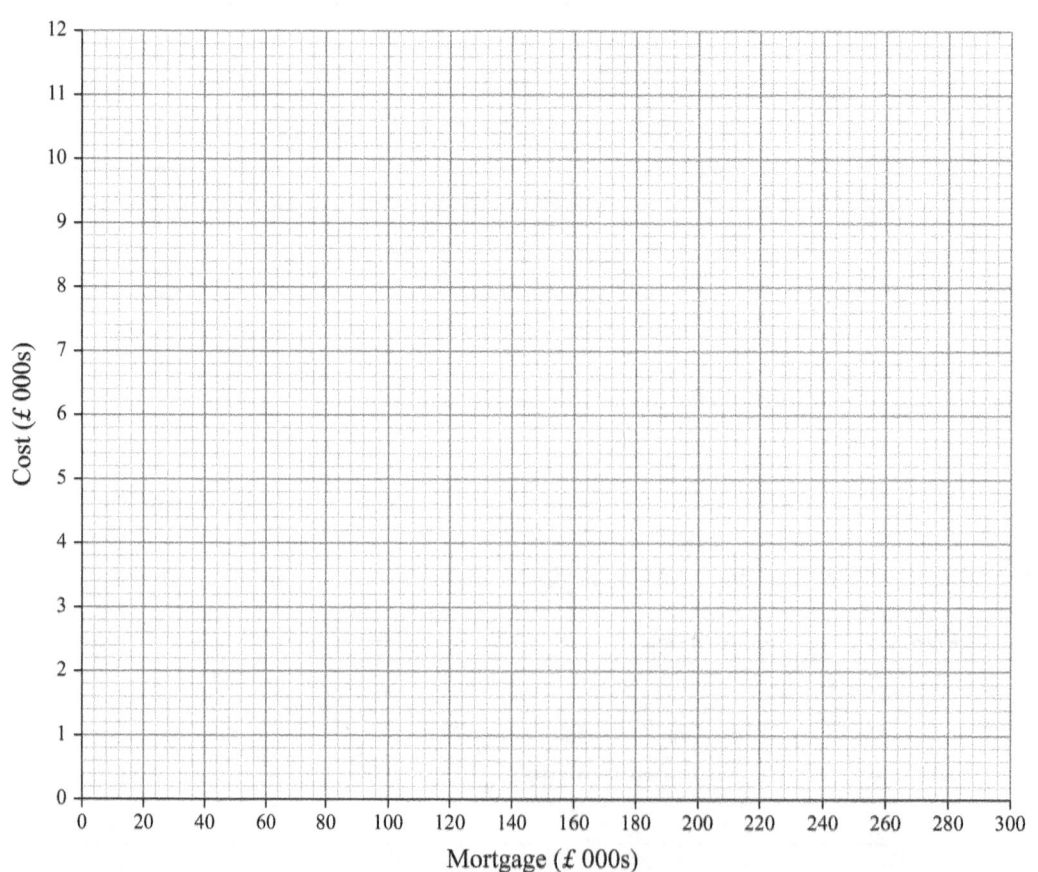

4 Apart from the Sun, Sirius is the brightest star as seen from Earth.

The *magnitude* of a star is a measure of its brightness and is defined in such a way that Sirius is $10^{0.4(M+1.46)}$ times as bright as a star of magnitude M.

(a) Polaris, the Pole Star, has magnitude 1.98. Compare the brightness of Sirius and Polaris.

[2 marks]

_____

_____

_____

_____

(b) The Sun has magnitude −26.74. Calculate how many times brighter than Sirius is the Sun.

[2 marks]

_____

_____

_____

_____

(c) What is the magnitude of Sirius?

[2 marks]

_____

_____

_____

_____

(d) Sketch the graph of $y = 10^{0.4(x+1.46)}$ indicating the coordinates of any points of intersection with the axes.

[2 marks]

5 Using a high-speed camera, the position of the tip of a chameleon's tongue was measured every millisecond and plotted on the graph. The tongue's maximum speed was reached after 10 milliseconds.

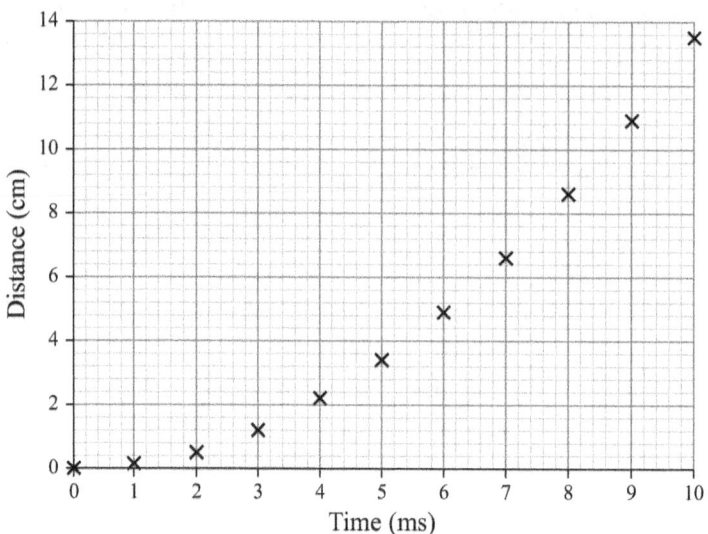

(a) Find the average speed (in m s^{-1}) of the tip of the chameleon's tongue.

[2 marks]

_____

_____

_____

_____

(b) Use the graph to find the maximum speed of the tip of the tongue.

[3 marks]

_____

_____

_____

(c) Find the average acceleration of the tip of the tongue.

[3 marks]

_____

_____

_____

_____

6 Professional sports pitches usually look perfectly flat.

However, many sports pitches are actually slightly raised in the centre so as to encourage rainwater to run off the pitch.

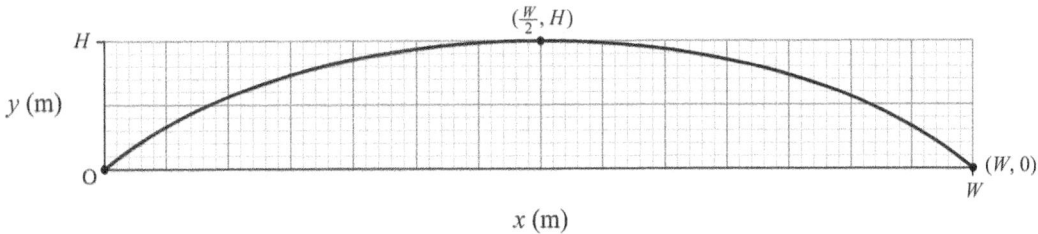

The cross-section of the sports pitch shown above has equation

$$y = 0.2 - a(x - 50)^2$$

(a) What is the length, Wm, of the pitch and what is the height, Hm, at its centre? Explain your answer.

[3 marks]

_____

_____

_____

_____

(b) Find the value of the constant a.

[3 marks]

_____

_____

_____

_____

7   In September 2016, Henrik Raimer set the world record skydiving speed of $167\,\mathrm{m\,s^{-1}}$.

You can assume that he had accelerated from 0 to $74.1\,\mathrm{m\,s^{-1}}$ in 10 seconds. You can also assume that his speed $v\,\mathrm{m\,s^{-1}}$ at time t seconds can be modelled by the exponential function

$$v = A + Be^{-kt}$$

for suitable constants A, B and k.

(a) Explain why $A = 167$

[1 mark]

_____

_____

(b) Find B and k. Hence find Henrik's speed after 20 seconds.

[7 marks]

_____

_____

_____

_____

_____

_____

_____

_____

_____

_____

_____

_____

_____

_____

_____

_____

_____

_____

Answers

ACTIVITY ANSWERS

Paper 1 and Paper 2 Common topics

Sampling methods and use of random numbers

1 (a) Trains that arrive in London between 7am and 9am

   (b) (i) Cluster

      (ii) Advantage: convenient; less expensive in time or money than visiting all stations

         Disadvantage: not representative because trains arriving at other London stations are omitted

2 Number the students in the class. Use a random number generator/button/tables.

   Use the first 5 numbers within the range, ignoring any repeats.

3 A representative sample reflects the whole population in relevant characteristics. In a general election, relevant characteristics could include gender, age, income, social grade, working status, location and ethnicity. An opinion poll that includes numbers of people in the same proportion as the whole population in terms of such characteristics is more likely to give a good prediction of the result of the election. A poll that is not representative of the population is more likely to predict incorrect results.

4 60

5 (a) Yes. The numbers of students in the age and gender categories in the sample will be proportional to those in the whole sixth form. The sample will be representative of the population and so results from it should reflect those that would have arisen from the whole population.

   (b) Number of male students—Year 12: 9, Year 13: 7

      Number of female students—Year 12: 8; Year 13: 6

6 The survey did not fairly represent both sets of staff since it included 28% from Nottingham University Hospitals but only 9.3% from Sherwood Forest Hospitals.

7 (a) The sample is too small and is not stratified.

   (b) Choose a larger sample, then use stratified sampling.

8 (a) All light bulbs made by the company

   (b) (i) All light bulbs do not have an equal probability of being selected.

      (ii) Ascertain how many bulbs will be produced in a batch or on a day and decide on the size of sample required. (To give the same size sample as that described in part (b) (i) would be 10% of any batch or day's production.) Use a random number generator/button/tables to find the positions of the required bulbs in the production line, ignoring any repeated random numbers.

9 (a) In both stratified sampling and quota sampling the population is divided into groups according to key characteristics and the proportion of the population in each group is used to calculate the number from each group that is needed to make up a sample of the required size.

   (b) In stratified sampling, a random method is used to select the items or people from each group, whereas quota sampling is usually done by a non-random method. Quota sampling is more likely to give a biased sample (for example, when market researchers choose those people who look most likely to agree to be interviewed).

10 These methods are not reaching a representative sample. Some people may not be included (for example, for phone polls those who are not at home or have their mobiles switched off, and for online polls those who don't use the internet). Some may be reluctant to take part. Those interviewed may not tell the truth. Late swing or 'floating voters' could vote on a decision they make after they take part in the poll. Those who said they would vote may not actually do that (for example, low turnout because of poor weather). The sample may be too small to give accurate results.

11 (a) The questionnaires will not give a representative sample of views because the percentages of questionnaires returned by each group are not equal (as shown by the calculations in the table).

	Men	Women
Age (years)	% of questionnaires returned	% of questionnaires returned
Under 35	$\frac{45}{220} \times 100 = 20.5\%$	$\frac{54}{316} \times 100 = 17.1\%$
35–64	$\frac{146}{609} \times 100 = 24.0\%$	$\frac{173}{876} \times 100 = 19.7\%$
65 +	$\frac{175}{558} \times 100 = 31.4\%$	$\frac{154}{597} \times 100 = 25.8\%$

   (b) (i) $\frac{747}{3176} \times 100 = 23.5\%$

      (ii) Face-to-face interviews may get a better response rate than use of the post or email. The housing association could offer a gift or prize draw to encourage people to respond.

12 The percentage of interviews that were held with customers of the top three mobile phone providers were:

EE: $\frac{198}{551} \times 100 = 35.9\%$, O2: $\frac{138}{551} \times 100 = 25.0\%$,

Vodafone: $\frac{99}{551} \times 100 = 18.0\%$

These percentages do not closely match the market share, but there are good reasons why this should not be expected: the times of year are not exactly the same and the customer base will change. The interviews were carried out with customers who had contacted their provider during the previous three months and it is not known how many of the customers actually did this—the proportion is not likely to be exactly the same for each provider. More information is needed before it will be possible to decide whether or not Ofcom used an appropriate sample.

Types of data and numerical measures

1 (a) quantitative, discrete, primary

   (b)

mode	range	median	interquartile range	mean	standard deviation
£750k	£25.75m	£3.15m	£4.27m	£5.83m	£9.25m

   (c) (i) The median is the best representative value as it is mid-way through the dataset. The mode is the very lowest value in the distribution.

      (ii) The football club may use the mean to indicate to footballers and the media that they are a comparatively rich club when compared with others. Or they may use the mode if their aim is to suggest to shareholders that they are very careful with money.

(d) The interquartile range is the best measure of spread in situations like this when both the range and standard deviation are distorted by very large (or small) outliers.

2 The table gives averages and measures of spread for the doctors' times with patients. In this case, the mean and standard deviation are the best measures to use as they include all of the data and there are no extreme outliers to distort the results.

	mode(s)	range	median	interquart-ile range	mean	standard deviation
Dr Brown	9, 10 min	9 min	9 min	3 min	8.66 min	2.22 min
Dr Green	10 min	10 min	10 min	3.5 min	9.31 min	2.46 min

On average, Doctor Green spends more time with patients, but the times vary more than those of Doctor Brown.

3 (a) continuous, secondary, quantitative

(b) The table gives estimated values for all EU countries from the given data.

modal group	median	interquartile range	mean	standard deviation
400 < w ≤ 500 kg/ person	460 kg/ person	550 − 383 = 167 kg/ person	468 kg/ person	122 kg/ person

At 482 kilograms per person, the UK average is higher than the estimated median and mean values and near the top of the modal group. This indicates that there may be some truth in the impression given by the headline that people in the UK create more waste than people in other EU countries. However, as the data is grouped, the mean and median values may not be very accurate and there is no information about how the data is distributed within the modal group. The sizes of the measures of spread indicate that there is wide variation in the data from different countries. So, while it is definitely true that people in the UK create more waste than those in the eight countries in the first two groups of the given table, there is not sufficient information to enable comparison with those in the other countries that are in the same group as the UK.

4 (a) Combined mean = 52.1 minutes (to 1dp)

(b) 180 minutes is an outlier—it would give a mean of
$$\frac{1301.9+180}{26} = 57.0 \text{ minutes (to 1dp)},$$ which is much higher than both of the given results and the combined mean. In this case, it would be better to exclude this value. A student who was absent on the day involved could have had much more time available for use of the mobile phone than the other students.

Box and whisker plots and cumulative frequency graphs

1 (a)

	Lowest age	Lower quartile (LQ)	Median	Upper quartile (UQ)	Highest age
Men	20	23	27	37	56
Women	18	24	29	36	51

(b)

Age of men and women in ballroom dancing class (years)

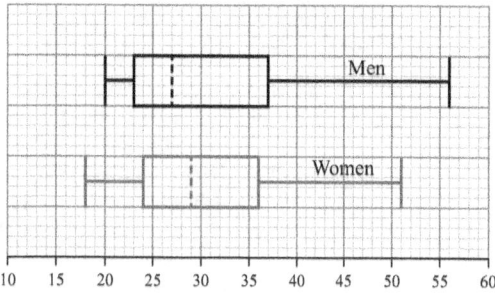

(c) The median age for men is 27 years and for women 29 years, indicating that on average the men were younger. The interquartile range (IQR) for men was 14 years and for women 12 years. The spread in the men's ages was greater than that in the women's ages.

2 (a) The median for the morning traffic was higher than that in the afternoon. The morning traffic was travelling faster on average than the afternoon traffic. The IQR was greater in the afternoon, indicating that the traffic speed was more variable in the afternoon.

(b) The median, quartiles and minimum and maximum speeds are easier to read from Simon's diagram, but there are reasons why Lily's diagram may be more useful in this situation. The cumulative frequency diagram shows how many vehicles were included in the survey and also allows you to tell how many were breaking the 20 mph speed limit and exceeding even higher speeds.

3 The median lengths are very similar. The IQR and range are both greater for the discus than the javelin throws. The discus and javelin throws were very similar on average, but the discus throws varied more in all except the second quarter of the distribution.

4

Cumulative frequency graph showing gross weekly earnings of employees of retail store chain

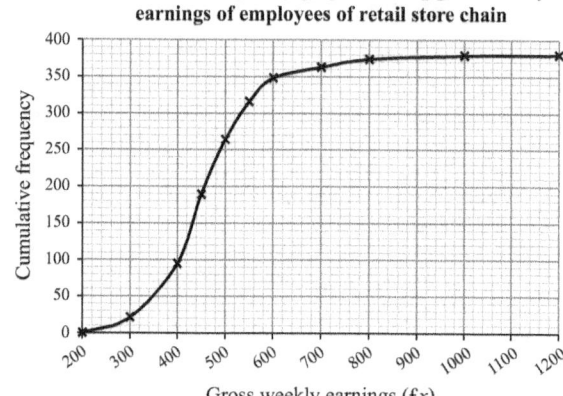

Gross weekly earnings (£x)

Approximate values for the percentiles from a CF graph (and their positions) are given in the table.

Percentile (position)	10th (38th)	25th (95th)	50th (190th)	75th (285th)	90th (342nd)
Full-time earnings (retail chain) 2sf	£323	£400	£451	£520	£590
Full-time earnings (UK)	£308.90	£389.20	£538.70	£762.40	£1057.70

The median full-time earnings is much lower in the retail chain than the UK average, indicating that on average the retail employees earn less. The IQR for the retail earnings is about £120, much less than the UK value of £373.20, showing that the spread of UK full-time earnings is far greater than that in the retail stores. Comparison of the other percentiles indicates that, at the lower end of the distribution, full-time earnings are more generous in the retail stores than the UK as a whole, whereas they are far less generous in the upper half of the distribution.

Histograms

1 (a) Jack has assumed everyone in Rutland is under 100 years old.

Age (years)	Frequency	Lower boundary	Upper boundary	Class width	Frequency Density
0–4	1766	0	5	5	1766 ÷ 5 = 353
5–17	5950	5	18	13	5950 ÷ 13 = 458
18–54	16322	18	55	37	16322 ÷ 37 = 441
55–64	4907	55	65	10	4907 ÷ 10 = 491
65–74	5013	65	75	10	5013 ÷ 10 = 501
75–89	3600	75	90	15	3600 ÷ 15 = 240
90+	488	90	100	10	488 ÷ 10 = 49
Total	38 046				

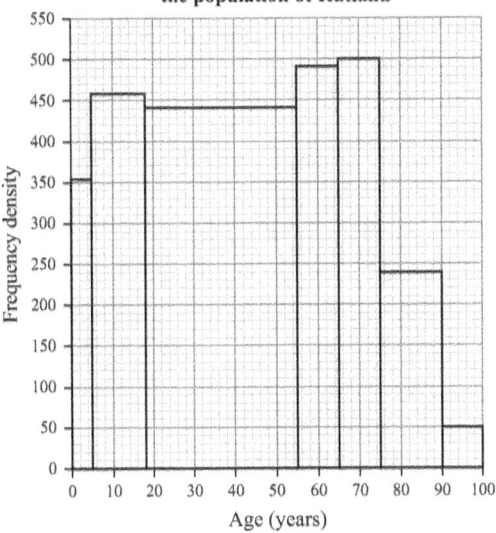

Age distribution of
the population of Rutland

(b) 20 people

(c) (i) 8600 people

    (ii) 30% (nearest %)

2 £434 700

Borrowing money

1 £5500

2 (a) The 45% APR is just used for illustration. A different rate might apply to particular borrowers.

    (b) £4350

    (c) $3000 = A\left(\dfrac{1}{1.45} + \dfrac{1}{1.45^2} + \dfrac{1}{1.45^3}\right)$

    Annual repayment = £2008.98

    Total repayment = £6026.94

3 (a) Investment for the future, greater security, can decorate/renovate as they wish

    (b) No savings for deposit/stamp duty, less risk and less responsibility, less hassle if you need to move

4 (a) £175 200   £7008.00   £12 000
      £170 208   £6808.32   £12 000

    (b) 2040

Budgeting

1 (a) Annual equivalent rate

    (b) £505.69

2 $\left(1 + \dfrac{0.0149}{12}\right)^{12} - 1 = 0.015$, i.e. 1.5%

The nominal rate ignores the compounding effect of earning interest on earlier amounts of interest.

3 (a) £2121.78

    (b) Nominal rate = 3.96%

       AER = 4%

4 (a) 14%

    (b) Assuming a working life of 40 years and that their income and expenditures do not change, the amount would be £280 × 12 × 40 = £134 400.

This ignores any interest earned. Assuming that they get 1 or 2% above inflation, this might increase their savings to about £200 000 in today's money. This amount might not, on its own, be sufficient to maintain their living standards in retirement. However, the most important aspect of these savings would be their availability before retirement to help with unexpected major expenditures. Also, as their family grows up and their circumstances change, their savings can change considerably.

Taxation

1 (a) £22 000

    (b) £84 500

2 (a) £82.50

    (b) 2.23% increase

3 (a) £195.36

    (b) £276.67

    (c) £49.50

    (d) Rate = Amount = Total gross pay = £2300

       Tax = £276.67, NI = £195.36, Student loan = £49.50,
       Total = £571.53

       Gross pay TD = £11 500, Tax TD = £1383.35,
       NI TD = £976.80, Pension TD = £250

       Student loan TD = £247.50

       Net pay = £1728.47

Student loans

1 Yes, she should! Unless she decides to re-enter the job market, this is a 'loan' on which she will never have to make any repayments.

2 (a) When the interest is added to the loan, the increased amount of the loan will only have the same buying power as the original loan.

    (b) $3\dfrac{(36\,000 - 21\,000)}{(41\,000 - 21\,000)} + 1.6\% = 3.85\%$

3 (a) £1080

    (b) £1496

    (c) £43 813.53

4 In this example, Clare's debt is seen to be increasing. In most circumstances this would be very worrying and could be seen as something which would put one off going to university and getting into this position. However, the wiping out of the debt after 30 years means that even someone with a respectable salary like Clare can end up never having to even repay the debt, never mind the interest. *Only those who earn a lot after graduating or leaving university will repay a lot.*

Percentage change

1 (a) £3 × 1.5 = £4.50

    (b) The factor is 1 − 0.25 = 0.75

       £P × this factor equals £4.50

    (c) £6

2 £3

3 £200 000

4 £22 000

5 $E = 1.25$ (euros to the pound)

6 100 pence

7 £110

Modelling and estimation

1 Keeping stock is expensive, both in terms of the money tied up in the stock and in terms of the cost of the warehouse, rates, computerised stock control systems and labour. Not keeping enough stock is expensive in terms of potential loss of sales and damage to the reputation of the business.

2 (a) $4D$

    (b) The sales have been assumed to be even throughout the year.

    (c) Keeping a buffer stock reduces the risk of shortfalls due to fluctuations in demand.

3 See answer to Question **1**

4 (a) $4D$ items have been bought at £A each.

    (b) There are 4 deliveries at £B each.

(c) The average level of stock is $S + \dfrac{D}{2}$

The cost is the same as the cost of holding $S + \dfrac{D}{2}$ items at

£C each for the year, i.e. $£\left(S + \dfrac{D}{2}\right)C$

5 £100 925

6 (a) The number of students on the course each year, n

The percentage who have a textbook, $p\%$

The cost of the book, £c.

The royalty percentage, $r\%$

(b) Number of students with a book each year $= \dfrac{np}{100}$

Royalties per book $= £\dfrac{cr}{100}$

Total $= £\dfrac{cr}{100} \times \dfrac{np}{100} \times \dfrac{l}{t}$

This can be simplified to $£\dfrac{crnpl}{10000t}$

(c) When the course ends, many of the books may not have had a full t years use. In practice, the numbers will fluctuate from year to year as the course becomes successful or declines.

7 (a) The Earth is a sphere of radius 6000 km. A step is 0.6 m. You can walk on water. Assume the surface is smooth.

(b) $\dfrac{2\pi \times 6 \times 10^6}{0.6} \approx 60$ million

8 2 million

Critical analysis

1 (a) The y-axis is numbered in a misleading way with the numbers decreasing away from the origin.

On the y-axis, –100% True does not make sense; it should be 0% True.

The title is misleading since the highest person on the graph is the least truthful and not the most.

Having two axes is irrelevant since they measure the same lack of truth.

(b) Nothing. *Politifact* is not responsible for how its data is used by others.

(c) $70 - 49 = 21$, not 31

The comparison is with Pence not Clinton. The figures are percentages not numbers of lies. A corrected statement might be: '*The percentage of Trump's statements that were lies was 21% more than the percentage of Pence's statements that were lies.*'

2 As a subsequent letter to the journal pointed out, an extremely small study of people interested in diets and who, in fact, already had relatively low cholesterol levels tells us nothing about the population at large. This was a biased sample.

3 It might be relatively hard to find pregnant women who would admit to drinking and there would be ethical issues about seeming to condone their drinking during the trial. A major difficulty is that pregnant women who do drink are ignoring well-publicised advice and therefore may have other health-related issues that could confuse the results of the trial.

4 If the results of only some trials are reported this could introduce significant bias into the database of results. This is actually the case, since the same NHS report indicated that trials with negative results were twice as likely not to be published as those with positive results.

Paper 2A topics

Normal distribution

1 (a) 0.993

(b) 0.023

2 (a) Assume that the marks are distributed normally. 13.6%

(b) 11 (or 12) students
$44 000 (or $48 000)

3 17

4 (a) $\mu = 250$, $\sigma = 0.4$

The rods have the same mean and s.d. as those from supplier X. Only choose to switch if other reasons indicate this, such as price or reliability of deliveries.

(b) 37

5 (a) Assume that BMIs are distributed normally.

Overweight

25 is 0.3 s.d. below the mean.

$\Phi(0.3) = 0.618$

This suggests 61.8% of adults are overweight compared to the actual 61.7%

Obese

30 is 0.7 s.d. above the mean.

$1 - \Phi(0.7) = 0.242$

This suggests 24.2% of adults are overweight compared to the actual 24.9%

Based upon these values for the mean and s.d., the calculated percentages are consistent with the known percentages. The normal model is therefore a reasonable one, at least for the overweight/obese range.

(b) This sample has mean 29.6 and s.d. 6.3.

This sample of people therefore have, on average, higher BMIs than the general population. This indicates that higher BMI will be correlated with diabetes. The BMIs of people in the sample are also somewhat more variable than those found in the general population. This indicates that there will be people with relatively low BMIs who still have diabetes.

6 (a) The first field has the ideal average pH value. However, the soil's pH is relatively variable in this field and an unsuitable pH of below 6.5 is within 2 s.d. of the mean.

The second field has mean pH 6.84 and s.d. 0.16. So, on average, the field's acidity is acceptable. The fact that an unsuitable pH of below 6.5 is more than 2 s.d. away from the mean makes it likely that a smaller area of this field would yield a poor crop.

(b) 5%

Confidence intervals

1 $\dfrac{\sigma}{\sqrt{n}}$

2 (a) 0.311

(b) 0.576

3 Mean of sample = 19.9

$19.9 \pm 2.33 \times 1.5 = (16.4, 23.4)$

4 $193 \pm 2.58 \times \dfrac{10}{\sqrt{12}} = (185.6, 200.4)$

The claimed mean is in this range. This one sample does not provide sufficient evidence to doubt the claim.

5 (a) The eight average scores have mean 105.5

The standard error of the mean is $\dfrac{20}{\sqrt{2}} \approx 14.1$. The variance is 200

(b/c) For the standard error of the mean to be applicable, the scores of one partner must be independent of that of the other. This is unlikely since a person is likely to be attracted to someone of a similar intelligence. The sample must be selected at random. However, selecting only married couples may well produce a biased sample since intelligence and marital status may not be independent.

Scatter graphs

1 (a) Mean point (42.5, 178)

(b) Gradient ≈ -0.6

Maximum heart rate reduces by 0.6 beats per minute for each extra year of age.

(c) (i) $H = 204 - 0.6n$

(ii) 75 years is outside of the data range used and extrapolation gives unreliable results. In this case the graph suggests that the line of best fit may overestimate maximum heart rate for men over 60 years old.

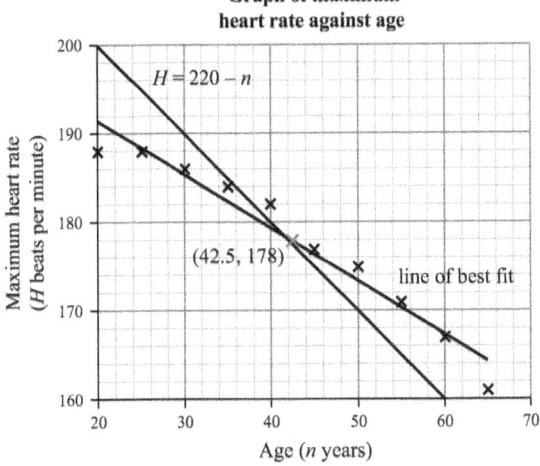

Graph of maximum heart rate against age

(d) The formula $H = 220 - n$ does not fit the data as well as the line of best fit. It overestimates the maximum heart rate for younger men and underestimates the maximum heart rate for older men.

(e) The data points appear to follow a curve, rather than a straight line. A quadratic function may give a better model.

2

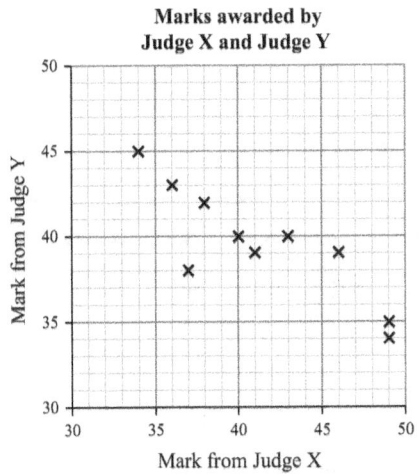

Marks awarded by Judge X and Judge Y

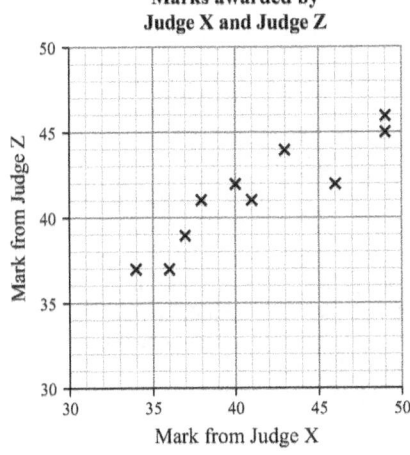

Marks awarded by Judge X and Judge Z

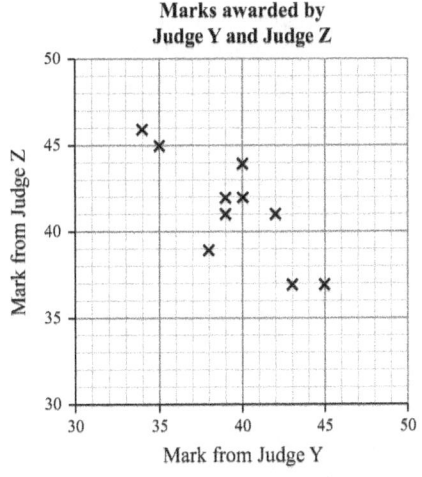

Marks awarded by Judge Y and Judge Z

The scatter graphs illustrate:

- strong positive correlation between Judge X's and Judge Z's marks
- strong negative correlation between Judge X's and Judge Y's marks
- strong negative correlation between Judge Y's and Judge Z's marks

This shows good agreement between Judge X's and Judge Z's marks, but that Judge Y's marks were out of line with both of the other judges.

Regression lines

1 (a) $H = 204 - 0.6n$

(b) Gradient ≈ -0.6

(c) Plotting the mean point, $(42.5, 178)$ and other points found from the equation gives the line shown.

(d) Comparison with student's own previous answers.

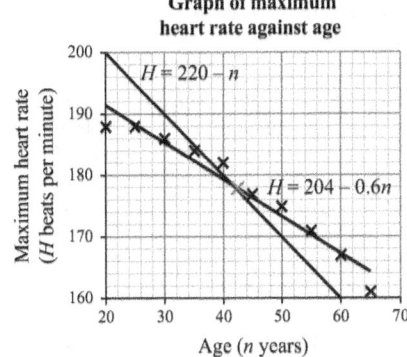

Graph of maximum heart rate against age

2 (a) $y = 0.667 + 0.207x$ (3sf) where x represents funding in millions of pounds and y represents the number of medals.

(b) The gradient is approximately 0.2. 0.2 medals per million pounds is equivalent to 1 medal for £5 million. However, there are a number of reasons why this is unlikely to be accurate. The correlation between funding and number of medals is not very strong. Many other variables influence the number of medals won in any particular sport, the most obvious of which is the ability of the sportsperson compared with that of other contenders.

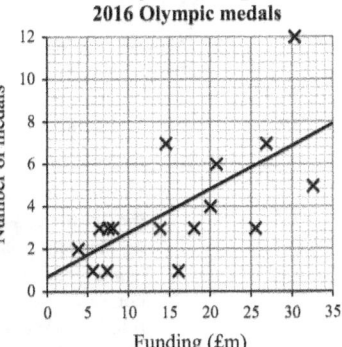

UK Sport funding and 2016 Olympic medals

3 (a)

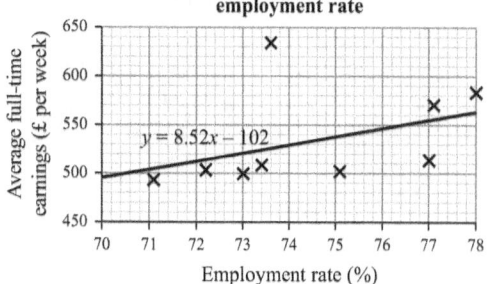

Average full-time earnings and employment rate

$y = 8.52x - 102$

(x-axis: Employment rate (%), y-axis: Average full-time earnings (£ per week))

(b) London

(c) (i) $y = 10.9x - 293$ (3sf)

   (ii) The line would be steeper and follow the other points more closely.

(d) Correlation between employment rate and full-time earnings is fairly strongly correlated for regions outside of London. London is unusual in having very high average full-time earnings.

Applications of the product moment correlation coefficient (pmcc)

1 Judge X and Judge Y marks: $r = -0.86$ (2dp)

   Strong negative correlation

   Judge X and Judge Z marks: $r = 0.92$ (2dp)

   Strong positive correlation

   Judge Y and Judge Z marks: $r = -0.82$ (2dp)

   Strong negative correlation

   This shows good agreement between Judge X's and Judge Z's marks, but that Judge Y's marks were out of line with both of the other judges.

2 Glucose and BMI: $r = 0.21$ (2dp)   Weak positive correlation
   Glucose and waist: $r = 0.86$ (2dp)   Strong positive correlation
   Use waist measurement—however, note that this is a small sample.

3 (a) (i) $r = 0.419$ (3sf)   **(ii)** $r = 0.805$ (3sf)

   (b) In both cases, the correlation is positive, but it is much stronger when London is excluded. This supports the answer given for Question **3** parts **(c)** and **(d)** in the regression lines activity. London is unusual in having a high average rate of pay that is less closely correlated with the employment rate. The average salary in London is unusually high because some highly-paid sectors of the economy are concentrated there (e.g. financial services in the city).

4 (a) (i) $y = 1.78x + 60.7$ (3sf)   **(ii)** $r = 0.706$ (3sf)

   (b) The gradient 1.78 suggests that an increase of 1% of GDP spent on health gives, on average, an extra 1.78 years of life to men. The correlation is fairly strong, indicating that there is a relationship between the percentage of GDP spent on health and male life expectancy, but that other factors will also influence this (e.g. diet, healthy lifestyle, genetic factors, etc.).

   (c) (i) $y = 0.853x + 74.5$ (3sf)   **(ii)** $r = 0.590$ (3sf)

   (iii) The gradient of 0.853 is less steep suggesting that an increase in the percentage of GDP spent on health gives less of an improvement in life expectancy for women than it does for men. The correlation is less strong, indicating a weaker relationship between the percentage of GDP spent on health and life expectancy for women than for men.

Paper 2B topics

Critical path analysis

1 (a/b)

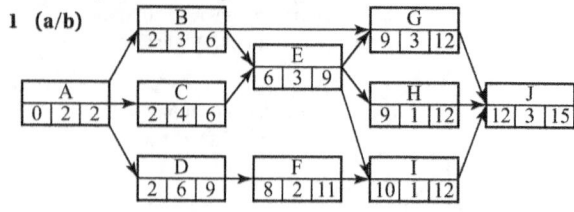

(c) A, C, E, G, J

(d)

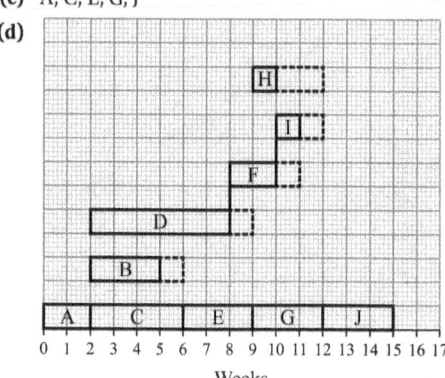

(x-axis: Weeks, activities A–J shown on Gantt chart)

(e) Start activities D, F, H as soon as possible. Start activity I as late as possible.

(f) Activity H has a float of 2 weeks so its delay has no effect. Activity D has a float of 1 week so its delay causes the project to be delayed by 1 week.

Venn diagrams

1 (a) 7   **(b)** $\dfrac{7}{17}$ **(c)** $\dfrac{3}{7}$ **(d)** $\dfrac{1}{2}$

   (e) 1.5

   (f) 82.4—This assumes the week shown in the diagram is typical in terms of students and activities on offer.

2 (a) $\dfrac{5}{47}$ **(b) (i)** $\dfrac{4}{5}$ **(ii)** $\dfrac{2}{5}$

   (c) Malta. Although $\dfrac{1}{47} \approx 2\%$, Malta has a small population ($\approx 400\,000$) compared to, for example, Russia. The total population of Council of Europe states is approximately 800 million. This gives a probability of only 0.05%.

Tree diagrams

1

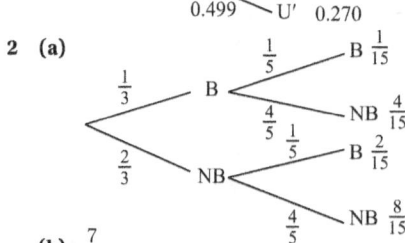

(0.458 W; 0.528 U 0.242; 0.472 U' 0.216; 0.542 W'; 0.501 U 0.271; 0.499 U' 0.270)

2 (a)

$\frac{1}{3}$ B $\frac{1}{5}$ B $\frac{1}{15}$; $\frac{4}{5}$ NB $\frac{4}{15}$; $\frac{2}{3}$ NB $\frac{1}{5}$ B $\frac{2}{15}$; $\frac{4}{5}$ NB $\frac{8}{15}$

   (b) $\dfrac{7}{15}$

   (c) The independence of the two record attempts has been assumed. This assumption is unlikely. For example, if the weather conditions are ideal for one runner they are likely to be good for the other.

3 **(a)**

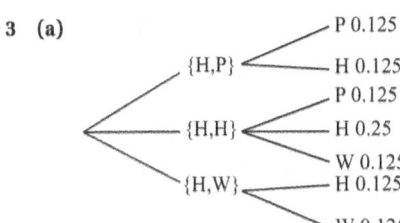

{H,P} — P 0.125, H 0.125
{H,H} — P 0.125, H 0.25, W 0.125
{H,W} — H 0.125, W 0.125

(b) $1:2:1$

(c) The type H (Hybrid) plants **look** the same as the type P plants. The first generation produced in the experiment were all type H and had purple flowers. The next generation were P, H, W in the ratio $1:2:1$ and so ¾ of them were purple.

Control measures

1 **(a)** The missing three probabilities are 0.16, 0.16 and 0.64

(b) £7200

(c) The delays must be independent. No control measures are taken.

(d) Completing on time is good for the builder's reputation.

2 **(a)** The missing penalties are both £4000

(b) Some of the extra workers may be able to help on both activities.

(c) The option with the lowest expected cost is to employ extra workers for *y* only.

Conditional probability

1 **(a)** $P(D \cap T) = P(D) \times P(T|D) = 0.01 \times 0.95 = 0.0095$

(b) $0.99 \times 0.01 = 0.0099$

(c) $0.0095 + 0.0099 = 0.0194$

(d) $P(D \cap T) = P(T) \times P(D|T)$

$0.0095 = 0.0194 \times P(D|T)$

$P(D|T) \approx 0.49$

(e) 25

2 $P(T) = 0.0001 + 0.9999 \times 0.01 \approx 0.0101$

$0.0001 = 0.0101 \times P(D|T)$

$P(D|T) \approx 0.01$

Any (understandable) concern should be mitigated by the fact that there is a 99% chance they do **not** have the disease. This is grounds for having further tests but not for immediate pessimism.

3 **(a)** $\frac{1}{4}$

(b) $\frac{3}{4}$

(c) $\frac{1}{3}$

Expectation

1 The expected winnings are £ $0 \times \frac{1}{4} + 4 \times \frac{1}{4} + 0 \times \frac{1}{6} + 2 \times \frac{1}{6} + 10 \times \frac{1}{6} =$ £3

A fair price is £3. This will only be the case if the person organising the game is not trying to make a profit.

2 £12.54 (this assumes that the top prize is £100 000)

3 **(a)** **(i)** 0.28, **(ii)** 0.54, **(iii)** 0.18

(b) 0.9

4 **(a)** 0.611

(b) This assumes that a person's probability of not turning up is independent of the actions of the other people who have signed up. This is a reasonable working assumption even though it is unlikely to be precisely true, e.g. for members of the same family.

(c) £11.10

(d) There are other possible benefits to **not** selling the extra ticket. For example, having only 29 tourists turn up may reduce the cost of refreshments if any are being provided. Also, the reputation of the company needs to be borne in mind. (However, the policy of overbooking is widespread in some contexts.)

Insurance

1 **(a)** Ron should book a standard site

(b) He should not pay this fee, since the extra cost outweighs the extra benefit.

2 **(a)** For probability *p*

Extra cost £4

Extra benefit £37.50 × *p*

These are roughly equal if $p = 0.1$. The protection appears worthwhile if the chance of the 'unforeseen circumstances' are greater than roughly 1 in 10.

(b) Illness is arguably by far the most likely 'unforeseen circumstance' that might qualify. On that basis, the extra benefit is now reduced to £7.50. The protection now appears worthwhile only if the chance of the 'unforeseen circumstances' are greater than roughly 1 in 2.

In fact, this example is based upon a story on *The Guardian* website (5 Nov 2016). The claim (effectively for £7.50) was not paid because of a condition in the small print. This type of insurance is a waste of money.

Paper 2C topics

Intersection points

1 **(a)** A straight line from *O* to $(14.8, 400)$

(b) 31.5 m. Assume constant acceleration.

(c) A curve from $(0, 100)$ to $(3, 131.5)$ and then a straight line to $(16, 405)$

(d) After approximately 11.4 seconds

(e) Just over 120 m

2 **(a)** British Gas — Line through $(0, 90)$ and $(2400, 370)$

EDF Energy — Line through $(0, 65)$ and $(2400, 375)$

First Utility — Line through $(0, 17.5)$ and $(2400, 455)$

(b) The low standing charge makes First Utility best for low-usage customers.

(c) Use First Utility if you expect your annual usage will be less than 925 kwh. Use EDF Energy if your usage is expected to be between 925 and 1860 kwh. Use British Gas if your usage is expected to be over 1860 kwh.

Gradients

1 **(a)** Gradient 3000

(b) In December 2014, the infection rate peaked at approximately 3000 new cases per month.

(c) The curve is initially close to the actual curve but is above it after Jan 2015. It models the first year of the outbreak very accurately but predicts that it would take longer to reduce the rate of infection. (Arguably, the comparison might indicate that more effective measures had been adopted by early 2015.)

2 **(a)** Gradient 3.2

(b) When production is 12 000 per month, the extra cost of producing each extra poussin is £3.20. (This is called the *marginal cost*.)

(c) To maximise profit, production should be increased to 12 000 per month. It should **not** be raised above that level since the extra cost would then be greater than the extra revenue.

Velocity–time graphs

1 (a) $70\,\mathrm{m\,s^{-1}}$

   (b) Because the arrow then has constant speed and is not being accelerated by the bow.

   (c) Approximately $17\,000\,\mathrm{m\,s^{-2}}$

2 (a) The arrow from the traditional bow gains speed first and reaches its maximum speed sooner. The arrow from the compound reaches a higher maximum speed.

   (b) The arrow from the traditional bow has a higher initial acceleration. This acceleration reduces from its maximum after 2 milliseconds to zero after 12 milliseconds. The arrow from the compound bow has a lower initial acceleration. This acceleration lasts longer and actually increases until after roughly 14 milliseconds.

   (c) The area under the graph for the traditional bow is greater than that for the compound bow.

   (d) Area of triangle + area of rectangle $\approx \dfrac{70 \times 0.006}{2} + 70 \times 0.012$

   ≈ 1 metre

Exponential functions

1 (a) 4010

   (b) 219 minutes

   (c) $500\mathrm{e}^{0.0347(t+20)} = 500\mathrm{e}^{0.0347t}\mathrm{e}^{0.0347 \times 20} = 500\mathrm{e}^{0.0347t} \times 2.002$

   The population has been multiplied by $2.002 \approx 2$

2 (a) Half the lambs will be male. On average, after 1 year, each ewe plus its one female offspring will be available for lambing. This assumes no losses due to weather, old age, selling to market, etc.

   (b) 50×2^n

3 (a) 1 metre

   (b) 2232

4 6.6 (years)

5 $\mathrm{e}^{10} \approx 22000$

   The gradient at a point on the graph of this function is equal to the y-value at that point.

Fitting quadratics

1 (a) $6 = c,\ 8 = a+b+c,\ 0 = 9a+3b+c$

   (b) $c = 6$

   (c) $a = -2,\ b = 4$

   (d) $y = -2x^2 + 4x + 6$

2 (a) $(2, 5000), (3, 17\,000)$

   (b) $a = 3000,\ c = -1000$

   (c) A loss of £1000

3 (a) $a = 120000,\ b = 200$

   (b) £50 because it gives the maximum profit of £120 000

Fitting exponentials

1 (a) $A = 20$

   (b) $20 + B = 100$

   $B = 80$

   (c) $20 + 80\mathrm{e}^{-23k} = 28$

   (d) $80\mathrm{e}^{-23k} = 8$

   $\mathrm{e}^{-23k} = 0.1$

   $k = \dfrac{\ln 0.1}{-23} \approx 0.1$

2 $y = 8 + 4\mathrm{e}^{-kx}$

   $k = 0.116$

3 (a) $y = 3\mathrm{e}^{-x} - 2$

   (b) $y = \mathrm{e}^{2x} - 5$

   (c) $y = 8 - \mathrm{e}^{5x}$

   (d) $y = 3 - 5\mathrm{e}^{-7x}$

PRACTICE PAPER ANSWERS

Short answers are intended as a quick check only. It is important that you check the full mark schemes available online at www.oxfordsecondary.co.uk/aqams-answers, which show you how to achieve full marks for each question.

Set 1 Paper 1

1 (a) continuous, quantitative

   (b) $\dfrac{60}{(600+60)} \times 100 \approx 9$

   (c) It is convenient. Confined elephants are unlikely to have the same sleep patterns as those in the wild.

   (d) Number the elephants 1 to N. Use a random number generator to choose a number from 1 to N. Repeat another eight times, ignoring repeated numbers.

2 (a) Loan + Interest = £30 000 × 1.046 = £31 380

   Repayment = £20 000 × 0.09 = £1800

   £29 580

   (b) The debt will reduce by roughly £420 per year. The debt will reduce by more as the debt decreases. However, the increase will be small for many years.

   (c) Fiona would not need to repay the loan whilst her income was lower than the threshold.

3 Egypt's median is 23/24 compared to 39

   Egypt's quartiles are 11 and 39 compared to 20 and 57

   Egypt has a much higher proportion of young people. UK has a much higher proportion of elderly people. Egypt's population is generally younger. Egypt probably has a higher birth rate. Egypt probably has a higher death rate.

4 Assume the meteorite falls vertically.

   Surface area of Earth is approximately $4\pi(6 \times 10^6)^2\,\mathrm{m}^2$

   Model person as rectangle 0.6 m by 0.3 m

   $\dfrac{(0.6 \times 0.3)}{(4\pi(6 \times 10^6)^2)} \approx 4 \times 10^{-16}$

5 (a) Income tax £32 000 × 0.2 + 2000 × 0.4 = £7200

   NI £(42 996 − 8064) × 0.12 + (45 000 − 42 996) × 0.02 = £4231.92

   $\dfrac{£(45\,000 - 7200 - 4231.92)}{12} = £2797.34$

   (b) Deductions from the £5000 are £5000 × 0.42

   The difference is £241.67 per month.

   This assumes she has the same allowance.

6 (a) $\dfrac{£100 \times 0.8}{100} = £0.80$

   £0.80 × 13 = £10.40

   (b) £0.80 × 365 = £292

   365 days in a year

   FCA rules apply to this longer loan period.

   (c) The answer to part (a) shows that the repayment of £110.40 is correct for the maximum possible interest. Wonga is conforming to the FCA rule. The answer to part (b) shows that the interest rate is 292%.

   (d) Not relevant: these loans are only for short periods.

   Relevant: some people take out these loans repeatedly over long periods.

7 Use of a reference point, e.g. wheelbase $\approx 2\,\mathrm{m}$

   Allowing for perspective, e.g. use of central lines

   Calculation of length of skid, e.g. 15 wheelbases $\approx 30\,\mathrm{m}$

   Use of table and consistent report, e.g. speed $\approx 45\,\mathrm{mph}$ and so the speed limit had been exceeded

Any two sensible assumptions/comments, e.g. this assumes the car had skidded to rest; if the car had not skidded to rest its initial speed would have been even higher; this assumes the car had skidded as soon as braking started.

Set 1 Paper 2 Common

1. (a) It was an exit poll reflecting opinion on the day.

   (b) It had wrongly predicted a majority for Remain.

   (c) $\dfrac{16141241+17410742(+25359)}{46500001} \times 100 = 72.2$, as stated

   $\dfrac{17410742}{16141241+17410742(+25359)} \times 100 = 51.9$, as stated

   Similarly for the Remain percentage. However, these are percentages of those who actually voted, not of the whole electorate.

   Assumptions: all 16–17 year-olds would have registered; 65% vote (the higher of the quoted turnouts); they vote 75% : 25% in favour of Remain (using the 18–24 estimate).

   Remain: 1.6 million $\times 0.65 \times 0.75 = 780\,000$

   Leave: 260 000

   Leave would still have had a majority of some three-quarters of a million.

2. (a) Cluster

   (b) Too small a sample

   Teachers on field trip unlikely to be representative of all staff

   (c) Having radii in the ratio of 3 : 1, for example, gives a misleading area ratio of 9 : 1. The diagram over-represents teachers who make up a small proportion of the college. Even if the results were representative, then there would be roughly 20 students for every teacher and so the majority would be for Remain.

Set 1 Paper 2A

3. $\bar{x} = 208.9$

   z value $= 1.64$

   standard error $= \dfrac{15}{\sqrt{10}}$

   $208.9 \pm 1.64 \times \dfrac{15}{\sqrt{10}}$

   [201.1, 216.7]

   215 lies in the interval.

   There is insufficient evidence that they have faster reaction times.

4. pmcc for For v Points is 0.78

   pmcc for Against v Points is -0.89

   Both are therefore strongly correlated with points. For is positively correlated and Against negatively. The strongest correlation is with Against. This shows the importance of a strong defence.

5. (a) 0.159

   (b) 6 days

6. (a) 3.54

   34.8

   (b) $P = 27.8N - 63.7$

   Line drawn for their equation

   (c) 47.5

   (d) In a different climate, the relationship is likely to be different. A nitrogen level of 2 would indicate an impossible negative proportion.

7. (a) Relative to O, the sugar content of J must have a lower mean. However, if it has greater variability, then there can be more of J's drinks with a very high sugar content.

   (b) Assume both sugar contents are normally distributed.

   J: 26.5 = Mean + 1.25s.d.   O: 26.5 = Mean + 1.5s.d.

   Probabilities   0.89435   0.93319

   $0.89435 \times 0.93319 \approx 0.835$

Set 1 Paper 2B

3. (a) £251 252.50

   (b) An amount considerably less than £251 252.50 would be life-changing for many contestants. The certainty of gaining such an amount would then be worth more than the chance of winning an even larger amount.

   (c) (i) £1252.50   (ii) £250 000

   (d) The contestant's expected gain must equal the sum of the two expected costs.

4. (a)

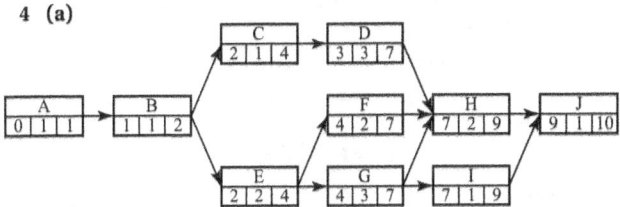

   (b) A B E G H J

   Speed up an activity on the critical path, e.g. bring in extra help on the core module programming.

   (c)

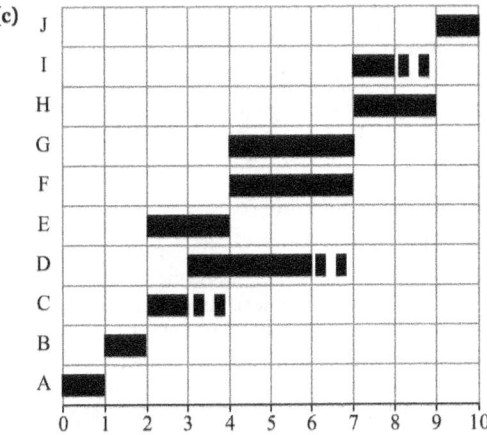

5. (a) Dodson & Fogg

   Gain 16K if win

   Expected gain (£K) $= 0.9 \times 16 - 0.1 \times 10 = 13.4$

   Jarndyce & Jarndyce

   Gain 18K if win

   Expected gain (£K) $= 0.8 \times 18 - 0.2 \times 10 = 12.4$

   Your expected gains are greater with Dodson & Fogg. If the website's figures can be relied on, then chose that firm.

   (b) The premium is likely to be in excess of £1000

6. (a) $\dfrac{5+8}{5+5+8+12} = \dfrac{13}{30}$

   (b) $\dfrac{12}{12+5+15+16} \times 100 = 25\%$

Set 1 Paper 2C

3. (a) Slows to rest

   Decelerates uniformly

   e.g. $v = 10 - t$

   (b) Starts from rest

   Accelerates at an increasing rate

   e.g. $v = t^2$

4. (a) $29\left(1 - \dfrac{40}{c}\right) = 14.5$

   $\dfrac{40}{c} = 0.5 \Rightarrow c = 80$

(b) Curve through $(11, 0)$ and $(40, 14.5)$

Slightly less curved than actual curve, supported by calculation(s)

e.g. at $x = 25$ and $x = 43$

5 (a) Line across from $\frac{3}{4}N$

Line down to x-axis

1.9 billion years

(b) 4.5 billion years (where the graphs cross). This assumes the Zircon was formed after the Earth had formed as a planet.

(c) At 4.5 billion years, the number of uranium atoms has halved, therefore $Ne^{-4.5k} = \dfrac{N}{2}$

Divide through by N, $e^{-4.5k} = \dfrac{1}{2}$

(d) $-4.5k = \ln\dfrac{1}{2}$

$k = 0.154$

(e) $N(1 - e^{-0.154t})$

6 (a) 5.4 hours

(b) 20

(c) The strength is increasing at a rate of 20% per hour.

(d) Sensible scale and labelled axes, quadratic through $(0, 0)$ and $(100, 0)$ and a maximum at $(50, 25)$

Set 2 Paper 1

1 (a) discrete, quantitative

(b) cluster

(c) Decide which characteristics of the population of drivers are relevant (e.g. gender, age). Choose a sample size and work out how many of the sample should be in each subgroup to be proportional to those in the population (according to government statistics). Select participants until the quotas are filled (e.g. approach drivers leaving test centres).

(d) Reasonable assumptions about the speed and time spent driving, e.g. 28 hours driving at average speed of 20 mph (low to include stops for discussion).

No extra driving practice

Distance = speed × time ≈ 28 × 20 ≈ 600 miles

2 (a) (i) Annual Percentage Rate   **(ii)** Annual Equivalent Rate

(b) (i) 15 years   **(ii)** Inflation

3 Alternative 1   Frequency = Frequency density × class width

For auditory stimulus

Reaction time (t milliseconds)	Number of adults
$160 \le t < 200$	6
$200 \le t < 220$	12
$220 \le t < 240$	28
$240 \le t < 260$	14
$260 \le t < 280$	12
$280 \le t < 320$	8
$320 \le t < 400$	0

Estimates of one average and one measure of spread

Stimulus	Modal class	Mean	Median	Range	Standard deviation	IQR
Visual	$240 \le t < 260$ ms	246 ms	245 ms	240 ms	34.2 ms	42 ms
Auditory	$220 \le t < 240$ ms	240 ms	236 ms	160 ms	31.1 ms	39 ms

Alternative 2

Frequency densities for a histogram showing reactions times to a visual stimulus:

= frequency ÷ class width

= 0.1, 0.7, 0.8, 1.15, 0.75, 0.15, 0.025

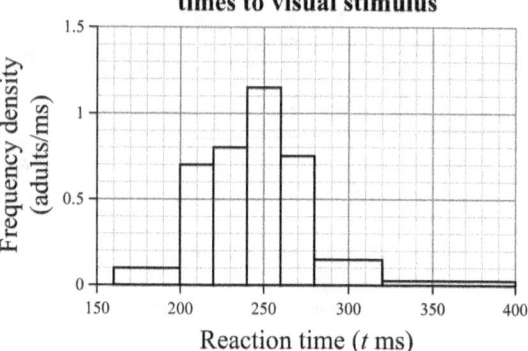

Histogram showing reaction times to visual stimulus

Comparison of main features in context (from either alternative): On average, reaction times to the visual stimulus were slower than those for the auditory stimulus. Reaction times to the visual stimulus were more variable than those for the auditory stimulus.

4   Income tax £$(34\,000 - 11\,000) \times 0.2 = £4600$

NI £$(34\,000 - 8064) \times 0.12 = £3112.32$

$\dfrac{£(34\,000 - 4600 - 3112.32)}{12} = £2190.64$

Sayed is correct

since $\dfrac{460}{2190.64} \times 100\% = 20.998...\%$ which is more than 20%

or because 20% of £2190.64 = £438.13 is less than the £460 rent.

5 (a) (i)   Interest = 4% of outstanding mortgage = 0.04 × outstanding mortgage

New outstanding mortgage = previous value + 0.04 × previous value

= 1.04 × previous value

Annual payment = 12 × monthly repayment

= 12 × £1600 = £19 200

(ii)

n	A_n (£)
0	140 000.00
1	126 400.00
2	112 256.00
3	97 546.24
4	82 248.09
5	66 338.01

(iii) £140 000 − £66 338.01 = £73 661.99

(b) At the end of each year Astrid would have paid less, so more interest would be added.

6 (a) Mean $= \dfrac{116 \times 1.4 + 64 \times 0.5}{116 + 64} = \dfrac{194.4}{180} = 1.08$ (hours per employee per week)

(b) (i) The mean is distorted by a small proportion of very high values, whereas the median is not.

(ii) Median = £506 (approx.) (less than the national value of £538.70)

Lower quartile = £415 (approx.)
Upper quartile = £568 (approx.)
IQR £153 (approx.)
National IQR = £762.40 − £389.20 = £373.20

The company's statement that on average their employees earn more than the national average is incorrect. The company's statement that their employees earnings are less varied than national earnings is correct.

7 **(a)** Advantage: convenient, cheap

Disadvantage: unlikely to be a representative sample of views, likely to be biased

(b) Sensible estimate of number of 3 and 4 year olds,

e.g. $\frac{2}{80} \times 96$ thousand ≈ 2 thousand

Assume take-up rate is 95% in this local authority (allow 100%)

Assume no new nurseries are needed/existing nurseries will accommodate the cover needed

Assume average staff cost is £20 000 per annum for 40 hours per week

Extra cost $\approx \dfrac{0.95 \times 2000 \times 570 \times £20000}{8 \times 40 \times 52}$

$\approx \dfrac{1 \times 2000 \times 600 \times £20000}{8 \times 40 \times 50}$ (following through from assumptions)

Extra cost $\approx £(1.3\text{–}1.5)$ million

Set 2 Paper 2 Common

1 **(a)** No key on either axis; no scale on vertical axis; a histogram should not have gaps between bars; the subdivision into just two groups does not display the data well

(b) Rounding errors; one lamb could be 1.05 kg and one just under 2.05 kg

2 **(a)** The graphs correlate very well. This supports statement B but not A. The graph for petrol prices is less erratic, also supporting statement B.

(b) Different horizontal scales; different units on the vertical scales; false zeroes on the vertical scales

(c) The price per litre would be 57.95p plus VAT

$57.95 \times 1.2 = 69.54$

(d) E.g. First peak $0.5 \times 67 + 85 \approx 119$

Second peak $0.5 \times 51 + 85 \approx 111$

Comment will depend upon the choice of points

(e) $0.5 \times 2 = 1$

'… *a 1p per litre change in the price of petrol.*'

Set 2 Paper 2A

3 Sample mean, $\bar{x} = \dfrac{248.5}{10} = 24.85\,\text{kg}$

z value for 98% confidence limits $= 2.3263$

Standard error $= \dfrac{0.3}{\sqrt{10}}$

98% confidence interval for $\mu = [24.85 - 2.3263 \times \dfrac{0.3}{\sqrt{10}},$

$24.85 + 2.3263 \times \dfrac{0.3}{\sqrt{10}}]$

$= [24.6, 25.1]$

25 kg is within this range, so there is not sufficient evidence to dispute the company's claim. (However, the sample is small and the sample mean is below 25 kg, so it would be advisable for the company to carry out further tests.)

4 **(a)** Gradient ≈ -13 (people per hectare per km)

The number of people per hectare reduces by 13 for each extra kilometre from the centre of town.

(b) -0.682 (3sf)

There is a fairly strong relationship between population density and distance from the centre of town, with the population density reducing as the distance increases.

(c) The range of distances covered by the given points is $[1.5, 3.7]$

3 km is within this range so the line of best fit is likely to give a reasonable estimate of the population density at this distance from the centre of town (although the fact that there were only eight given points casts some doubt on this). Both 0.5 km and 6 km are outside of this range and estimates of the population density from the line of

best fit at these distances are likely to be even less reliable. (It would be much better if the student used population and area estimates to work out the population densities in these suburbs.)

5 **(a)**

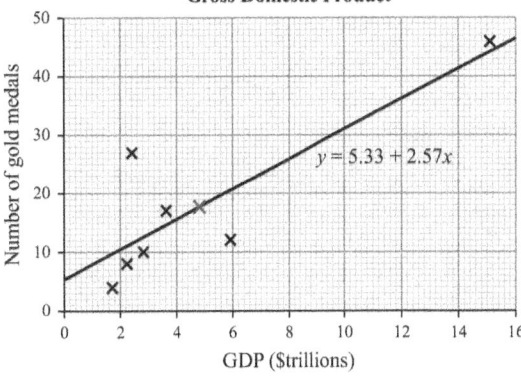

Gold medals at the 2016 Olympics against Gross Domestic Product

(b) $y = 5.33 + 2.57x$ (3sf)

(c) If above, the country has won more gold medals than its GDP would suggest and if below, the country has won fewer gold medals than its GDP would suggest.

6 **(a)** Using the pmcc: UK shoe sizes and foot length $r = 0.9999$

EU shoe sizes and foot length $r = 0.9981$

Using scatter graphs:

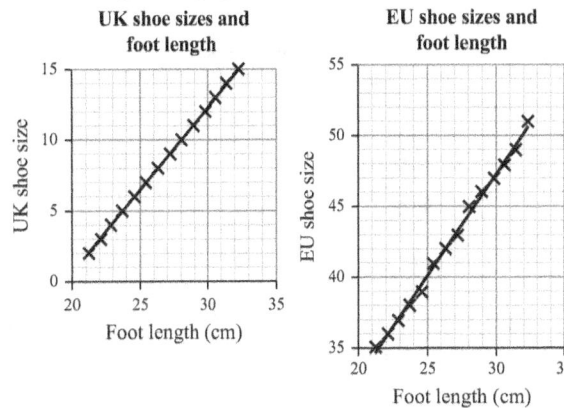

In both cases the correlation is extremely strong, but the relationship between UK shoe sizes and foot length is slightly stronger than that between EU shoe sizes and foot length.

(b) Assuming foot length follows a normal distribution, the company should make UK shoe sizes 3, 4, 5, 6, 7 and 8.

7 Assume the weight of the eggs, X grams, follows a normal distribution.

Total income $= £195.80$

Set 2 Paper 2B

3 **(a)** £72

(b) You know in advance what your costs are (although the companies have a variety of limitations and exclusions). You have (almost) no risk of a large unexpected cost. The cost of insurance is (much) greater than the expected costs of repairs. This outweighs the other arguments. [*Which?* concluded that warranties are a 'waste of money'.]

4 **(a)** Male full-time workers

(b) 0.2

(c) $\dfrac{1}{2} \times \dfrac{1}{4} = \dfrac{1}{8}$

This is not correct because being male and part-time are not independent. The correct answer is 7%.

(d)

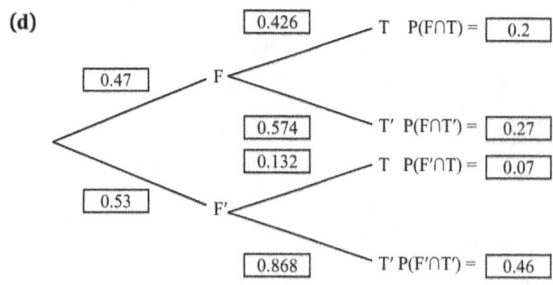

T $P(F \cap T) =$ 0.2

T' $P(F \cap T') =$ 0.27

T $P(F' \cap T) =$ 0.07

T' $P(F' \cap T') =$ 0.46

5 E.g. median and mean

Mean (advantage)—it takes into account all salaries.

Mean (disadvantage)—it is affected by extremely high salaries, e.g. of some female executives.

Median (advantage)—tt gives a salary that can be considered typical.

6 (a)

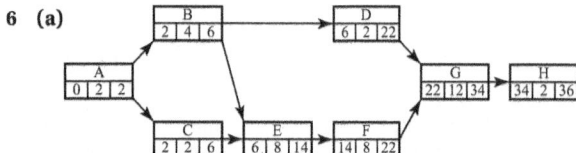

(b) A B E F G H

36 hours

(c)

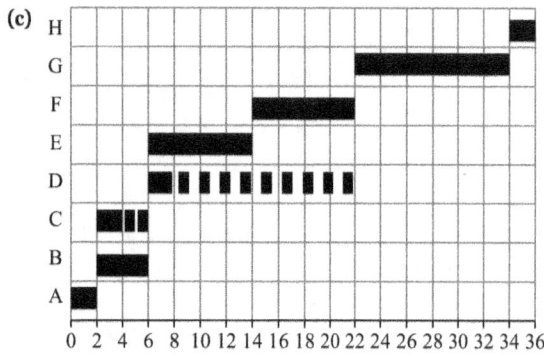

(d) He must take 36 hours on the critical path. On top of this, he must do C and D.

38 hours [Allow 40 hours if justified]

Assume that we do not count any rest periods and that D can be done towards the end of the drying period for the gloss.

7 (a) Total cost of B − Total cost of A = £500 − 0.05P

This is positive for $P < 10\,000$ and so A is then better. Otherwise B is better.

(b) Total cost of A − Cost of doing nothing = £500 − 0.1P

$P < 5000$	Take no measure
$5000 < P < 10\,000$	Take measure A
$10\,000 < P$	Take measure B

[Allow ≤ throughout]

Set 2 Paper 2C

3 (a) £1881 + 1370 + 1370 = £4621

(b) $C = 1881 + 0.0274A$

(c) Line through approximately $(0, 485)$ and $(100, 4065)$

Line through approximately $(0, 1881)$ and $(100, 4621)$

Costs are the same for a mortgage of £166 000 (more precisely £166 190)

For smaller amounts use Ingotts; for larger amounts use Borsetshire Building Society

This assumes the costs are the same once the 2-year fix has ended.

4 (a) Sirius is $10^{1.376} \approx 24$ times as bright as Polaris

(b) The Sun is $10^{-10.112} \approx 7.73 \times 10^{-11}$ times as bright as Sirius

(c) $1 = 10^{0.4(M+1.46)}$ and so $M = -1.46$

(d) An exponential curve through $(0, 3.84)$

5 (a) $13.5\,\mathrm{m\,s^{-1}}$

(b) $26\,\mathrm{m\,s^{-1}}$ (approx. $30\,\mathrm{m\,s^{-1}}$)

(c) $2600\,\mathrm{m\,s^{-2}}$ (approx. $3000\,\mathrm{m\,s^{-2}}$)

6 (a) The maximum value of y is when $x = 50$

Therefore $W = 100$ and $H = 0.2$

(b) $a = \dfrac{0.2}{50^2} = 8 \times 10^{-5}$

7 (a) For large t, $v \approx A$ and so $A = 167$

(b) $B = -167$

$k \approx 0.0586$

$115\,\mathrm{m\,s^{-1}}$